STEVENSONS
2010
Foreword by the First Minister

*I would like to welcome you all to the **15th edition** of Scotland's **Good Hotel and Food Book** 2010. Tourism has experienced a mixed year. The economic difficulties that have been felt around the world have undoubtedly had an impact here in Scotland, however, I believe that the majority of our businesses have worked extremely hard to minimise the impact of these challenging times. Our Year of Homecoming is well underway and I am sure it has already been very successful in bringing visitors back 'home' to Scotland. Many of these will have been fortunate to enjoy some of the finest accommodation and exquisite cuisine that we have on offer.*

Now more than ever, quality is paramount in making the visitor experience a truly memorable occasion. From the welcome and service that visitors receive, the cleanliness and conditions of an establishment, to the general ambience and friendliness portrayed, all these details are essential to encourage visitors to return time after time.

This book contains Alan Stevenson's personal collection of some of the finest hotels and restaurants across Scotland. Once again, he has travelled the length and breadth of the country in search of the very best that Scotland has to offer. I hope that you find this book useful in helping you choose where to stay and dine and I hope that you have a very pleasant time.

ALEX SALMOND

FOREWORD

STEVENSONS
SCOTLAND'S
GOOD HOTEL AND FOOD BOOK
2010

Published by:
Alan Stevenson Publications
Fala
20 West Cairn Crescent
Penicuik
Midlothian
EH26 0AR
Tel: 01968 678015
Mobile: 07786 966341
Email: alan@stevensons-scotland.com
www.stevensons-scotland.com

North American Representative:
Ann Litt,
Undiscovered Britain
11978 Audubon Place
Philadelphia, PA 19116
Tel: (215) 969-0542
Fax: (215) 969-9251
Email: ann@undiscoveredBritain.com
www:UndiscoveredBritain.com

Consultant: James Chassels

Copyright © 2009 Stevensons - Scotland's Good Hotel and Food Book - Fifteenth Edition

ISBN 978-0-9550877-4-5

Price: £8.00
    $16.00 from USA agent only. (Includes Canada)

Typesetting/Graphics: Colin Shepherd.
Proof Administration: Katie Fenton of Aviemore Business Solutions.
Printed in Scotland: Woods of Perth Ltd.
Front Cover: The Four Seasons Hotel, Perthshire.

Alan Stevenson
Publisher

*Absolutely delighted that my **15th edition** has the endorsement of **The First Minister for Scotland**. (See main Foreword on page one). Also the endorsement of **Albert Roux** who kindly penned the Food Foreword for me. (See page 68). After all this is a 'Scottish Publication' and our association with France forms what we still call The Auld Alliance between our two countries.*

Despite the recession and 'credit crunch' or whatever you want to call it the Country House hotel market has been as robust as ever. Ample evidence this year that many people stayed 'at home' although many took different holiday options such as self catering, camping & caravanning. During the months of August & September many hotels were finding it difficult to cope and had to turn people away. It's a pity we have to cram all our holidays into such a short period! This is the only time that many people, especially families, can take their holidays.

*Again I have included some old favourites within my personal selection with a few additions. Some, for one reason or another, have been deleted. Many will be known to you personally – a warm welcome assured and the care and comfort of the guest are paramount. Again I am grateful to my sponsors for their support of which a list appears on page 4. Please also see my newsletter on pages 10 and 11 which brings you up to date with some of the activity taking place around the country. Again I look forward to the **16th edition** of **STEVENSONS** for 2011. Enjoy.....*

Photo by Yerbury of Edinburgh

INTRODUCTION

STEVENSONS

SCOTLAND'S
GOOD HOTEL AND FOOD BOOK
2010

CONTENTS

Trade Sponsors

The Scotch Beef Club is unashamedly based on quality.

We do not use growth hormones in any shape or form.

We offer independent assurance, supported by the Scottish SPCA.

Our members believe strongly in animal welfare.

Our standards are much higher than legislation demands.

Fresh meat is low in salt and high in iron.

Our members are passionate about red meat.

Less stressed animals provide better tasting meat.

We are supported by some of the UK's finest chefs.

Cattle are reared mainly outdoors and fed on a grass diet.

All our livestock are born and raised for all of their lives on assured farms in Scotland.

Modern breeding and butchery standards produce leaner meat.

LOOKING FOR A REASON TO TRY A SCOTCH BEEF CLUB RESTAURANT? WELL, HERE'S TWELVE.

Our member restaurants are a cut above the rest. That's why they choose the finest Scotch Beef. With full traceability and guaranteed levels of assurance, Scotch Beef is high on quality, high on taste. So if you care about your food, look for the Scotch Beef Club logo on your next meal out. We can think of at least a dozen reasons why.

To find a member restaurant near you, visit: www.scotchbeefclub.org

THE
SCOTCH BEEF
CLUB

STEVENSONS

SCOTLAND'S
GOOD HOTEL AND FOOD BOOK
2010

AWARDS/SYMBOLS
VisitScotland (Scottish Tourist Board)

The Star System is a world-first. It denotes quality assurance on a range of 1 to 5 stars. This is why it is only the quality of the welcome and service, the food, the hospitality, ambience and the comfort and condition of the property which earns VisitScotland stars, not the size of the accommodation or the range of facilities. Gold stars recognise businesses which constantly achieve the hightest level of excellence within their VisitScotland star rating. This business has excelled in the areas of customer care and hospitality and displays evidence of a real commitment to staff development and training.

The quality grades awarded are, eg:

★★★★★	Exceptional, world-class
★★★★	Excellent
★★★	Very Good
★★	Good

AA Red Rosettes 🏵🏵🏵🏵🏵

Hotels and restaurants may be awarded red rosettes to denote the quality of food they serve. It is an award scheme, not a classification scheme. They award rosettes annually on a rising scale of one to five.

AA Red Stars ★★★★★

The AA top hotels in Britain and Ireland are assessed and announced annually with a red star award. They recognise the very best hotels in the country that offer consistently outstanding levels of quality, comfort, cleanliness and comfort care. Red stars are awarded on a rising scale of one to five. Restaurants with rooms also qualify for this award.

Bull Logo

Any establishment which displays the Bull Logo is a member of the Scotch Beef Club. The criteria is strict - the product is derived from cattle born, reared for all of their lives, slaughtered and dressed in Scotland. The animals will have been produced in accordance with assurance schemes accredited to European Standard and meeting the standards and assessments set by Quality Meat Scotland's Assurance Schemes.

PLEASE NOTE: THESE AWARDS DO NOT NECESSARILY FORM PART OF MY OVERALL PERSONAL SELECTION OF GOOD HOTELS AND RESTAURANTS IN SCOTLAND. THEY ARE INCLUDED TO ASSIST THE VISITOR SELECT HIS/HER HOTEL OR RESTAURANT OF CHOICE. THE AWARDS ARE NOT MANDATORY FOR SELECTION TO THIS PUBLICATION.

SCOTLAND'S SPECIALIST SELLING AGENTS TO THE HOSPITALITY TRADE.

Commercial

Licensed premises sought
to fulfil demand following
excellent sales successes
in 2009

Commercial

Please call me to discuss sales prospects for
your business or for a confidential meeting
without obligation or fee.
Paul T Hart, Head of Commercial Sales
07799 896931

Local Knowledge - Global Marketing

Sales - Legal - Funding

ASG Commercial for an all inclusive one stop service.

York House, 20 Church Street, Inverness, IV1 1ED.
Tel: 0845 4500 790 Fax: 01463 711083
www.asgcommercial.co.uk
info@asgcommercial.co.uk

STEVENSONS

SCOTLAND'S
GOOD HOTEL AND FOOD BOOK
2010

HOW TO LOCATE A HOTEL OR RESTAURANT

1. First look at the map of **Scotland on page 12.** The place name of the hotels or restaurants I am featuring will be highlighted in bold type. Restaurants will be highlighted with a red circle. ●

2. Once you have pinpointed your location *follow along the top of the pages,* which are arranged alphabetically, until you arrive at your location.

3. If you already have the name of the hotel or restaurant and wish to know if it is included, turn to the index at the back of the book. Hotels and restaurants are listed alphabetically.

4. In some cases where hotels and restaurants are located close to major towns, they may be shown under that town with the exact location in brackets. For example, **ABERDEEN (Oldmeldrum).**

5. **Hotel Price guide:** This quote is based on an overnight stay single & double. Normally this is for bed & breakfast but sometimes if dinner is included it will be indicated. (includes dinner). Also applicable to restaurants with rooms.

**View from
The Four Seasons Hotel**

6. The above prices are quoted for a one night stay, but most of the establishments in this book offer reductions for stays of two or more nights. Also please enquire about seasonal bargain 'breaks'.

7. **Symbols/Awards.** Awards from VisitScotland (Quality Assurance Classification), AA red food rosettes & stars and the Bull Logo (Scotch Beef Club - Quality Meat Scotland) appear on hotel and restaurant entries. See introductory pages for a full explanation of these symbols and awards.

STEVENSONS

Every year certain changes take place eg., hotels bought and sold, retirements, staff changes, developments and in some cases closures where the country house reverts to a private residence. This was certainly the case at **Kinnaird** when Mrs Constance Ward announced her retirement in August. A family estate since 1927 Mrs. Ward took up residence in 1975 and opened the hotel in 1990. It became a favoured spot for the elite and a member of the prestigious Relais & Chateaux group of which there are only 4 others in Scotland. Another retirement announced (in advance) is that of Patricia Davies at **Culloden House** which takes place in April 2010. Patricia has been at Culloden House for 16 years and joined when it belonged to Iain and Marjory McKenzie. Apart from reception duties she seemed to be everywhere –front of house, in the dining room, doing the accounts and taking reservations!! We wish her well.

Meldrum House & Country Estate continue with their major development of the golf and country estate including the complete overhaul of the stable block which increases the bedroom capacity to 22 (9 in the main hotel) Now described as a "mini Gleneagles" it is very impressive. The **Hebridean**

Princess continues to trade extremely well despite administration problems earlier in the year. Matthew Gray, head chef at **Inverlochy Castle** for many years has moved to America and Phil Carnegie has been promoted from sous to head chef. Jane Watson (Operations Manager) also at Inverlochy Castle celebrates her 30th year of service and Rosina Barr (head housekeeper) celebrates her 29th year at the Castle. An extraordinary record indeed. **Pool House** has reverted from hotel status to 5 Star Guest Accommodation. The **Glenmoriston Arms Hotel** is now under new ownership – Paul & Sue Hudson. Kevin Dalgleish (head chef) of **Forss House/Ackergill Tower** has been awarded a second AA rosette. Daren Campbell (ex- head chef at Andrew Fairlie) has been appointed head chef at **Fortingall Hotel**. Gregor MacKinnon has been appointed General Manager at **The Manor House**, Oban. The driveway and parking area at **Roman Camp Country House** has been fully tarred!

Finally, it was with great sadness that the death of John Smither (**Arisaig House**) was announced earlier this year. John was an inspiration not only to me but to many other people. He advised me in my "early years" and encouraged me to publish my own book. I will always be grateful to him – he always kept in touch after he retired. Our condolences to his wife Ruth & family.

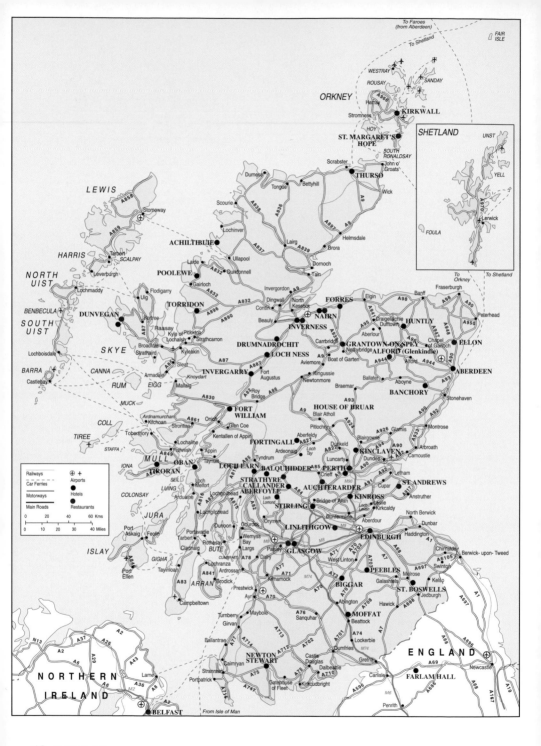

THE MARCLIFFE HOTEL, SPA AND RESTAURANT

North Deeside Road, Aberdeen. AB15 9YA
Tel: 01224 861000   Fax: 01224 868860
Email: reservations@marcliffe.com   www.marcliffe.com

This is an outstanding property perfectly positioned in the attractive 'leafy' suburb of Cults on the outskirts of Aberdeen. Just off the main road to Braemar it is situated in 11 acres of magnificent woodland and garden policies (with ample parking I should add). Indulged myself this year with a 2 night stay. Bedrooms range from executive to two room suites and are beautifully appointed. Superior furnishings in each suite with modern facilities such as satellite TV and modem points. Menus are sophisticated using the natural larder of Aberdeenshire - renowned for its agriculture and fish outlets. Scottish Lobster is a firm favourite (whole or half) and also the surf 'n' turf option of fillet of beef with lobster. Don't forget the jumbo Russian King Crab (all the way from Murmansk!). Wine cellar of note to match and bar stocked with over 100 malt whiskies. Ideal to explore the whisky and castle trails, and never far away from a golf course. Gymnasium and beauty spa offering a selection of treatments. This hotel is a member of Small Luxury Hotels Of The World and Connoisseurs Scotland. A truly memorable experience.

Open: *All year*
No. Rooms: *42 En Suite 42*
Room telephones: *Yes*
TV in Rooms: *Yes*
Pets: *Yes*   **Children:** *Yes*
Disabled: *Yes*

Gymnasium/Beauty Spa: *Yes (see above)*
Conference Facilities: *Extremely good*
Price Guide: *Single £155.00-£345.00 (suite)*
Double £175.00 - £345.00 (suite)
Location: *Aberdeen ring road, turn west at A93 - to Braemar.*
Hotel is 1ml on right. Aberdeen airport 25mins.

Haggarts of Aberfeldy

Since 1801 Haggarts have been making and supplying Tweed. These Tweeds are renowned throughout the UK and beyond for their hard wearing and warm qualities making them most suitable for country pursuits. Today we continue to stock these Country Tweeds alongside much finer and softer fabrics more suitable for Sport Jackets and Casual Wear.

We specialise in the tailoring of Sporting Garments for Hunting, Shooting & Fishing as well as Sports Jackets from a range of much finer cloths.

A selection of Tweed Sports Jackets, Shooting Coats, Woollens & Cashmeres are always available from stock.

We also stock a full range of Highland Dress and will be delighted to make a kilt in your family tartan.

32 Dunkeld Street
Aberfeldy
Perthshire
PH15 2AB

Tel: +44(0)1887 820306   Fax: +44(0)1887 820055
Email: enquiries@haggarts.com

For trade customers please contact us for our full range.

MELDRUM HOUSE HOTEL (GOLF AND COUNTRY ESTATE)

Oldmeldrum, Aberdeenshire. AB51 0AE
Tel: 01651 872294 Fax: 01651 872464
Email: enquiries@meldrumhouse.co.uk www.meldrumhouse.co.uk

There has been a major undertaking this year to restore the 17th century stable block which, many of you will remember as a ruin. This has been meticulously restored to facilitate more bedrooms, a conference facility and a chapel. Conveniently positioned opposite the hotel it blends in perfectly with the 350 acres of garden and woodland which include water features and an abundance of wildlife. A planned refurbishment of the hotel itself is also planned - my overnight stay was most enjoyable once again. Bedrooms are full of character with quality furnishings, are spacious, and have excellent en suite facilities. The locally sourced food is of the highest calibre and very consistent; there is a great ambience in the dining area. Wonderful venue for weddings and corporate meetings (away from all the buzz!) this country estate with golf course offers top quality services to meet the modern demand. Don't forget the 5 'chain lodge' bedrooms which offer more privacy for that longer stay. Well recommended – your host and General Manager: Peter Walker.

Open: *All year*		**Swimming Pool/Health Club:** *No*	
No. Rooms: *22 En Suite 22*		**Conference Facilities:** *Yes*	
Room telephones: *Yes*		**Price Guide:**	*Single £100.00 - £130.00*
TV in Rooms: *Yes*			*Double £120.00-£150.00*
Pets: *Small dogs* **Children:** *Yes*		**Location:**	*Main gates on A947 (Aberdeen to Banff Rd) 1*
Disabled: *Yes*			*mile north of Oldmeldrum. 13mls north of airport.*

Michael Jones - Head Chef
Lake of Menteith

LAKE OF MENTEITH
(HOTEL & WATERFRONT RESTAURANT)
Port of Menteith, Perthshire. FK8 3RA
Tel: 01877 385258
Email: enquiries@lake-hotel.com www.lake-hotel.com

This hotel is situated in the most idyllic and picturesque position one could wish for – right beside the only Lake in Scotland. The 'image' and interior of this hotel have been transformed in recent years from what I remember. Decorated in the warm and welcoming style of a classic New England waterfront hotel, with muted tones and the extensive use of local timber and stone in the restaurant and bar. Proprietor Ian Fleming has been working to upgrade this property for nearly 4 years. Bedrooms and en suite facilities had nearly all been upgraded when I stayed - to a high standard I should add - comfort of the guest a priority. In addition, to the discerning traveller, the Lake Hotel will provide facilities for small corporate meetings and exclusive weddings. The food and beverage operation is one of the best in the country. Under the watchful eye of head chef Michael Jones, the waterfront restaurant serves seasonal, local produce thoughtfully and imaginatively prepared. Ian uses all his previous knowledge to maintain a consistency that will be recognised by other agencies. Only a short drive from Glasgow or Edinburgh.

Open: *All year*	**Swimming Pool/Health Club:** *No*
No. Rooms: *16*	**Conference Facilities:** *24 Director level*
Room telephones: *Yes*	**Price Guide:** *Single £80.00 Double £130.00 – £160.00*
TV in Rooms: *Yes*	**Location:** *Turn off M9 at Junct. 10 onto A84, follow to A873*
Pets: *No* **Children:** *Yes*	*signposted Aberfoyle. On to Port of Menteith then*
Disabled: *Yes*	*left down the B8034. Hotel 250 yds on right.*

Chris Firth-Bernard - Head Chef
Summer Isles Hotel
(Michelin Star)

SUMMER ISLES HOTEL

Achiltibuie, Ross-shire. IV26 2YG
Tel: 01854 622282   Fax: 01854 622251
Email: info@summerisleshotel.com   www.summerisleshotel.com

Once again great anticipation when planning my annual trip to The Summer Isles Hotel. Under new ownership the team is led by Duncan & Aurelie Evans with **Michelin star** Chris Firth-Bernard and his kitchen brigade. Although classed as a food destination, careful investment over the years provides bedrooms/suites of a superior quality – quite stunning really with magnificent views. Overnight stay this year was as good as ever. A firm favourite, you feel as though you are 'bonding with nature' in this isolated part of Scotland under the gaze of Stac Polly. 15 miles of single track road opens up spectacularly to the marvellous beach at Achiltibuie and The Summer Isles beyond. The dining experience is so well executed as one would expect – cheese board beyond expectation and a mouth watering sweet trolley completes the perfect experience. Seafood a speciality. Wine cellar of note.   Stay awhile and explore the area with magnificent sunsets – peace and contentment. Sister hotel – Bunchrew House Hotel in Inverness. (see separate entry and also Chris's recipe at rear of book).

Open: *26th March - 31st October incl.*	**Children:**	*Yes*
No. Rooms: *13 En Suite 13*	**Disabled:**	*Yes*
Room telephones: *Yes*	**Price Guide:**	*Single £110.00-£170.00*
TV in Rooms: *Suites and large seaview*		*Double from £140.00-£200.00 Suite £260.00*
rooms only	**Location:**	*A835 to Ullapool. 10 miles north of Ullapool*
Pets: *By arrangement*		*turn left onto single track road to Achiltibuie.*
		15 miles to village.

Kinloch Anderson
SCOTLAND

Foremost Experts
in
Highland Dress
Since 1868

Kinloch Anderson
Commercial Street/Dock Street
Leith, Edinburgh, EH6 6EX, Scotland

Tel: +44 (0) 131 555 1355 / 1390
www.kinlochanderson.com

MONACHYLE MHOR

Balquhidder, Lochearnhead, Perthshire. FK19 8PQ

Tel: 01877 384622 Fax: 01877 384305

Email: info@monachylemhor.com www.monachylemhor.com

If you require a rural and romantic destination allied with comfort, service and excellent cuisine head for Monachyle Mhor at Balquhidder. Only 4 miles from the village itself this property enjoys a spectacular position overlooking Loch Voil and Loch Doine. The estate itself covers 2000 acres and is the domain of Tom Lewis (chef/proprietor) His culinary skills are well known - using fresh produce from the estate or his own organic garden Tom produces dishes which demonstrate complete dedication. I was very impressed with the new refurbished accommodation – also the conversion of the Courtyard cottages with wood burning stoves, central heating, fully equipped kitchens, TV, video and CD stereo. I have known the Lewis family for some years now – always a warm welcome with roaring log fires and this atmosphere extends throughout this 18th century 'farmhouse'. Situated in the heart of the Trossachs (Rob Roy country whose grave is at Balquhidder) with magnificent scenery all around you this is the perfect place base to stay and travel. Member of The Scotch Beef Club.

Open: *All year*	**Disabled:** *Dining only*
No. Rooms: *10 (2 cottages)*	**Swimming Pool/Health Club:** *No*
Room telephones: *Yes*	**Conference Facilities:** *No*
TV in Rooms: *Yes*	**Price Guide:** *Double £110.00-£160.00*
Pets: *No*	**Location:** *11 mls north of Callander on A84. Turn right at*
Children: *Yes*	*Kingshouse Hotel - 6 mls straight along Glen road.*

Jeff Purves - Head Chef
Banchory Lodge Hotel

BANCHORY LODGE HOTEL

Banchory, Kincardineshire. AB31 3HS
Tel: 01330 822625 Fax: 01330 825019
Email: enquiries@banchorylodge.co.uk www.banchorylodge.co.uk

A former 18th century coaching inn, it commands a stunning position on the banks of the River Dee. The gardens reflect the care and attention taken by resident proprietor Margaret Jaffray with sweeping lawns down to the river bank and an abundance of flowers (especially the daffodils in spring). This care and attention continues its theme within the hotel. The bedrooms are very spacious and comfortable - designed with considerable flair and imagination. Many have views over the river. The dining room is a masterpiece. Creative menus from Head Chef Jeff Purves include Dee salmon and Aberdeen Angus beef as one would expect in this area. Exclusive use of the hotel for weddings (ideal venue) and corporate meetings are welcomed. An old favourite of mine, I have some wonderful memories of this establishment in years past. After 42 years Margaret has retained the values of good hotel keeping of which, she is rightly, very proud.

Open: *All year*	**Swimming Pool/Health Club:** *No*
No. Rooms: *22 En Suite 22*	**Conference Facilities:** *Up to 30*
Room telephones: *Yes*	**Price Guide:** *Single £95.00 Double £170.00*
TV in Rooms: *Yes*	**Location:** *A93 North Deeside road from Aberdeen.*
Pets: *Yes* **Children:** *Yes*	*Turn down Dee Street from Main Street -*
Disabled: *No*	*400 yards - hotel on your left.*

SKIRLING HOUSE

Skirling, Biggar, Lanarkshire. ML12 6HD
Tel: 01899 860274   Fax: 01899 860255
Email: enquiry@skirlinghouse.com   www.skirlinghouse.com

This house, built in 1908, was designed by the famous architect Ramsay Traquair for Lord Carmichael as a country retreat. Skirling is a small attractive village just outside Biggar on the A72 to Peebles and the property is situated by the village green. The house has retained the original theme with carvings, rich fabrics, antiques and fine paintings - a feature is the 16th century Florentine carved ceiling which is much admired by guests. Bob and Isobel Hunter have made this an oasis of great comfort, quality cuisine and hospitality and there is a very informal but friendly and relaxing atmosphere. The award of 5 stars Guest House from VisitScotland is fully merited - bedrooms are tastefully decorated in keeping with the house and offer every comfort. The house menus (dinner is a set menu) change daily and make excellent use of fresh seasonal produce from the garden. Good selection and a sound quality of food with fine farmhouse cheeses. Meals are served in the conservatory with views over the magnificent lawn and gardens to the rear. (also with herb garden) A very skilled operation here and highly recommended. Only a short distance from Edinburgh.

Open: *March - December*	**Price Guide:** *Single £85.00-£110.00 (inc. dinner)*
No. Rooms: *5 En Suite 5*	*B&B £55.00-£80.00*
Room telephones: *Yes + WiFi*	*Double £155.00-£180.00 (inc. dinner)*
TV in Rooms: *Yes*	*B&B £95.00-£120.00*
Pets: *Yes* **Children:** *Yes*	**Location:** *2 mls from Biggar on A72 overlooking*
Disabled: *Yes*	*village green.*

ROMAN CAMP COUNTRY HOUSE

Off Main Street, Callander, Perthshire. FK17 8BG
Tel: 01877 330003 Fax: 01877 331533
Email: mail@romancamphotel.co.uk www.romancamphotel.co.uk

This country house, just off the main street in Callander, (just be careful at the entrance) is set amongst wonderful woodland and garden and rippling river nearby. Quite a haven in itself. Originally built in 1625 for the Dukes of Perth as a hunting lodge it still retains that aura – roaring log fires to welcome you with extremely comfortable public rooms to enjoy that afternoon tea. Each of the 15 bedrooms have their own distinctive theme – spacious and comfortable with nice extra 'touches'. Apart from a great afternoon tea, head chef Ian McNaught, well-known for his culinary skills, provides meals using quality ingredients adding flair and imagination in keeping with an AA 3 rosette award. Well-placed to tour the Trossachs which is an area of outstanding beauty in Scotland. No doubt an ideal venue for weddings (on an exclusive basis is recommended). Staff always extremely professional and friendly. A major improvement this year has been the upgrade of the entrance/exit driveways and the car park. I have that 'feel good' factor when I stop here for a blether with resident proprietors Eric & Marion Brown who are renowned for their attention to detail and a warm welcome.

Open: *All year*	**Swimming Pool/Health Club:** *No*
No. Rooms: *15 En Suite 15*	**Conference Facilities:** *Up to 100*
Room telephones: *Yes*	**Price Guide:** *Single from £85-£145*
TV in Rooms: *Yes* **Pets:** *Yes*	*Double from £135-£205*
Children: *Yes*	**Location:** *East End of Callander. Main Street from*
Disabled: *Yes*	*Stirling turn left down drive for 300 yards.*

AA ✿ ✿ ✿

UNRESERVED INDULGENCE

For further information on products by Gilchrist & Soames please contact:
•Tel: 01733 384118 •Fax: 01733 384101

GILCHRIST & SOAMES®
Est LONDON, ENGLAND
"World class amentities for world class hotels."

ULLINISH COUNTRY LODGE

Struan, Isle of Skye, Inverness-shire. IV56 8FD
Tel: 01470 572214   Fax: 01470 572341
Email: enquiries@ullinish-country-lodge.co.uk   www.ullinish-country-lodge.co.uk

My parents brought me on holiday to this area (Ose) in the late 40's and early 50's and I return every year to experience the grandeur of skerries, sea eagles and wild ocean spray. If you want to 'get away from it all' Ullinish Country Lodge is the ideal place to just 'chill out' as they say now. Now classified as a 'restaurant with rooms' this country lodge offers extremely high standards of hotel keeping. I have stayed here on 3 occasions – 4 of the bedrooms are quite spacious and luxurious and 2 are smaller but very snug and cosy. All the extra touches as you would expect from a 5 star establishment. I really like the lounge area with open fire where canapes are served before dinner. Great dinner menu and chef makes good use of local ingredients such as Speyside Beef and there is an emphasis now on seafood which couldn't be more local. From loch & sea to the plate! AA 3 rosette restaurant – expectations are high for this award. Exact technique, balance and depth of flavour are important. There can be no doubt that Brian & Pamela Howard have taken this country lodge to a new level. A short distance from Dunvegan Castle (home of The MacLeods) other places to visit are Glenbrittle, Portnalong and Elgol in the south. Staffin & Uig in the north.

Open: *All year except Jan*	**Swimming Pool/Health Club:** *No*
No. Rooms: *6 En Suite 6*	**Conference Facilities:** *No*
Room telephones: *No*	**Price Guide:** *Single from £90.00*
TV in Rooms: *Yes*	*Double from £130.00*
Pets: *No* **Children:** *Over 16*	**Location:** *9 miles south of Dunvegan on*
Disabled: *Dining only*	*Sligachan Road*

LOCH NESS LODGE HOTEL

Drumnadrochit, Inverness-shire. IV63 6TU
Tel: 01456 450342   Fax: 01456 450429
Email: info@lochness-hotel.com   www.lochness-hotel.com

Dating back to around 1740, this unusual hotel is synonymous with the famous Loch from which it takes its name. Once the home of a colonial tea planter, it stands in eight acres of delightful woodland grounds. Situated 14 miles from Inverness, it is a favourite spot for tourists. The hotel offers elegant en suite bedrooms and fresh imaginatively prepared food. The restaurant serves a fusion of modern and traditional cuisine: local venison, wild mushrooms and fresh garden vegetables. The hotel is linked to the Visitor Centre with its unique exhibition which attracts people from around the world. The management are now actively marketing their corporate facilities (wi-fi etc.) - this is the ideal venue for such an occasion away from the 'hustle and bustle' of city life and a short drive from Inverness. Log fires, friendly staff, outstanding cuisine and first class service make a holiday at the Loch Ness Lodge Hotel a memorable experience. Your host: Gillian Skinner.

Open: *Closed mid Oct - mid March*	**Swimming Pool/Health Club:** *No*
No. Rooms: *50 En Suite 50*	**Conference Facilities:** *Max. 120*
Room telephones: *Yes + WiFi*	**Price Guide:** *Single from £65.00 p.p.p.n.*
TV in Rooms: *Yes*	*Double from £90.00 per room per night*
Pets: *No* **Children:** *Yes*	**Location:** *14 miles south of Inverness on Fort William*
Disabled: *Dining only*	*Road.*

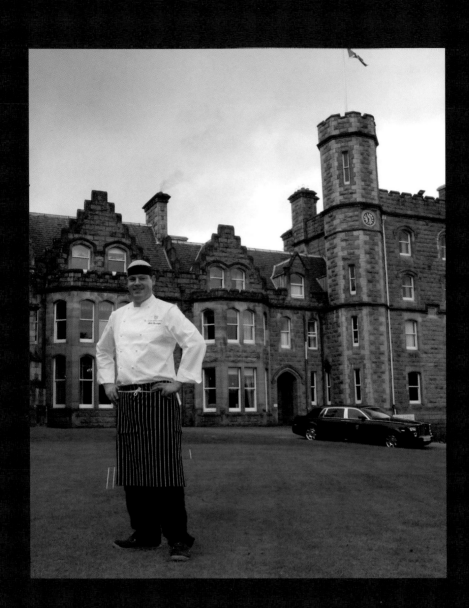

Phil Carnegie - Head Chef
Inverlochy Castle, Fort William
(Michelin Star & 3 AA Rosettes)

INVERLOCHY CASTLE

Torlundy, Fort William. PH33 6SN
Tel: 01397 702177 Fax: 01397 702953   USA Toll Free Tel: 1-888 424 0106
Email: info@inverlochy.co.uk www.inverlochycastlehotel.com

What can I say? Another wonderful 2 night stay at Inverlochy Castle - cannot find the words to describe such an experience. Perfect in all aspects. All bedrooms have quality furnishings and décor and the en suite bathrooms are a revelation – just exudes comfort. A truly outstanding property set in magnificent landscaped gardens it nestles below Ben Nevis in a stunning highland setting. A member of the prestigious Relais & Chateaux this hotel retains all the finest traditions of hotel keeping. The talents of head chef Phil Carnegie are obvious - high technical skills with flair and imagination. No disappointments and perfectly executed as reflected by the **Michelin Star**. The whole dining experience one to remember. Service could not be faulted. During her visit in 1873 Queen Victoria wrote in her diaries, "I never saw a lovelier or more romantic spot". There is a peaceful enduring ambience about Inverlochy Castle – a warm welcome by staff, peace and seclusion, with cuisine and wine cellar of the highest order. Host of activities in the area including one of the busiest ski resorts in Scotland. Your hosts Calum Milne & Jane Watson. Sister hotel: Rocpool Reserve, Inverness (see separate entry). Indulge yourself…….

Open: *All year.*	**Swimming Pool/Health Club:** *No*
No. Rooms: *18*	**Conference Facilities:** *Yes*
Room telephones: *Yes*	**Price Guide:** *Single £250-£350; Double/Twin £390-£490;*
TV in Rooms: *Yes*	*Suite £490-£650.*
Pets: *Yes* **Children:** *Yes*	**Location:** *3 miles north of Fort William. In the village*
Disabled: *No.*	*of Torlundy on A82.*

RAMNEE HOTEL
Victoria Road, Forres, Moray. IV36 3BN
Tel: 01309 672410 Fax: 01309 673392
Email: info@ramneehotel.com www.ramneehotel.com

This fine Edwardian mansion built in 1907 is situated in landscaped gardens to the east of the Royal Burgh of Forres. The Ramnee enjoys a certain amount of isolation but is in easy reach of the town centre which is famous for its parkland floral displays and architectural qualities. This hotel is operated by the Dinnes family-experienced hoteliers known to me for over 20 years. This is reflected with a VisitScotland 4 star classification. The bedrooms are a delight, (with 4 poster if required) - elegant, and very comfortable, all with en suite facilities - many have views over the Moray Firth. Scottish cuisine with a slight French influence using only the best of local produce - menus are varied to suit your appetite - there is imagination and flair used in the preparation and you will not be disappointed whether dining formally or taking a bar lunch/supper. There is a friendly atmosphere which radiates throughout the hotel. Golfing is high on the list of sporting activities in this area and businessmen make good use of the conference/seminar facilities, whilst the hotel is also now offering a selection of luxury, serviced bungalows in and around Forres.

Open: *All year.*	**Disabled**: *Dinner only*
No. Rooms: *18 En Suite 18*	**Swimming Pool/Health Club:** *No*
Room telephones: *Yes + WiFi*	**Conference Facilities:** *Theatre up to 100*
TV in Rooms: *Yes*	**Price Guide:** *Single £80-£120 Double £85-£160*
Pets: *Yes*	**Location:** *A96 Aberdeen-Inverness off by pass at roundabout*
Children: *Yes*	*to east side of Forres - 500 yards on right*

FORTINGALL HOTEL

Fortingall, Aberfeldy, Perthshire. PH15 2NQ
Tel: 01887 830367   Fax: 01887 830367

Email: hotel@fortingallhotel.com   www.fortingallhotel.com

Had my eye on this one for sometime and am now delighted to include it in my personal selection for edition 2010. Quite a unique location in a small village but surrounded by woodland and magnificent views to the hills looking down Glen Lyon. The Glenlyon Estate, which is a working farm, supplies most of the produce for the kitchen. Head chef Darin Campbell (ex head chef at Andrew Fairlie's) has a dedicated approach – sound technical skills using seasonal fresh ingredients. Good wine cellar to complement an excellent meal, whether fish, meat or game. Nice ambience in the dining room and in fact throughout the hotel. Enjoyed chatting to the locals in the popular Ewe Bar which is positioned at a discreet distance from the residents lounge. Superior furnished bedrooms with excellent en suite amenities and views over the hills. Shooting and stalking can be arranged on the Glenlyon Estate. Also fishing permits for salmon and trout are available. Or just take a tour of the estate itself with a picnic lunch. I really enjoyed my overnight stay here – very friendly atmosphere. Staff very helpful. Ideal for that small and exclusive wedding. Please enquire about seasonal breaks. Reduced rates for 2 nights or more. Your host: Roddy Jamieson.

Open: *All year*	**Disabled:** *Dining only*
No. Rooms: *10 En Suite 10*	**Swimming Pool/Health Club:**
Room telephones: *Yes*	**Conference Facilities:** *Up to 40*
TV in Rooms: *Yes*	**Price Guide:** *Single £134.00-£157.00, DBB*
Pets: *Yes*	*Double £218.00-£264.00, DBB*
Children: *Yes*	**Location:** *3 miles from Aberfeldy on the B846.*

UPLAWMOOR HOTEL & RESTAURANT

Neilston Road, Uplawmoor, Renfrewshire. G78 4AF
Tel: 01505 850565   Fax: 01505 850689

Email: info@uplawmoor.co.uk   www.uplawmoor.co.uk

"This unassuming small village hotel/inn is a real wee gem" writes James Chassels who did the overnight stay for me. "The sort of place you seek out but seldom find and so close to the airport and 12 miles from the city centre". A former 18th century coaching inn it still retains a bit of that aura (snug with open fire and comfortable with good fayre). Stuart and Emma Peacock have been here for 17 years and established a first class operation – the recent award of 3 gold stars (new award) from VisitScotland bears testament to the consistency they have achieved over these years. There are 14 extremely comfortable bedrooms with attractive fabrics and all with the expected facilities. Flat screen TV with DVD's supplied. The refurbished dining room has a contemporary rustic feel to it – or you can eat more informally in the spacious lounge bar. A Thistle Award finalist in the natural cooking of Scotland category Uplawmoor is renowned for its cuisine – great care and attention with sourcing of fresh ingredients and the skills of head chef Ewan McAllister complete the task. A la carte, table d' hote at £25:00 or Sunday lunch (very popular) plus bar meals are the options. Great rural location – good location for exploring the area so stay awhile and enjoy. Excellent value for money. (also see recipe at rear of book)

Open: *All year*	**Swimming Pool/Health Club:** *No*	
No. Rooms: *14 En Suite 14*	**Conference Facilities:** *small private meetings*	
Room telephones: *Yes*	**Price Guide:** *Single £60.00*	
TV in Rooms: *Yes*	*Double £85.00-£95.00*	
Pets: *Guide dogs only* **Children:** *Yes*	**Location:** *From Glasgow (12 mls). Exit at M77 to Jct. 2,*	
Disabled: *Dining only*	*then 8mls (follow signs)*	

AA❀ ❀

CASTLE HOTEL

Huntly, Aberdeenshire. AB54 4SH
Tel: 01466 792696   Fax: 01466 792641
Email: info@castlehotel.uk.com   www.castlehotel.uk.com

Although it has taken 10 years of hard work and investment the Meiklejohn family have now restored this majestic building to its former splendour. Formerly a home of the Dukes of Gordon this 18th century structure stands in 7 acres of woodland and sweeping lawns in the heart of 'the castle trail' just off the main Aberdeen to Inverness road and a short drive from Aberdeen airport. All bedrooms and suites have been upgraded to a high standard – the suites are particularly spacious and quite luxurious in all aspects. Large en suite facilites. The views from most of rooms and the dining room are spectacular. Enjoy a pre-dinner drink in the aptly named Distillery Bar (this area is part of the whisky trail) and sample traditional Scottish cuisine with fresh produce from the renowned agricultural area of Aberdeenshire, not to mention the marine harvest of its coasts. Truly a family enterprise Andrew & Linda together with son Stuart and daughter Nikki take an active role with tours organised around this scenic area. Other options could include golf, fishing, trekking or hillwalking. Area steeped in history – an abundance of castles to visit. Service was very courteous and friendly – a very warm welcome and most enjoyable experience.

Open: *All year*
No. Rooms: *18 En Suite 18*
Room telephones: *Yes*
TV in Rooms: *Yes*
Pets: *No*   **Children:** *Yes*
Disabled: *Limited*

Swimming Pool/Health Club: *No*
Conference Facilities: *5 up to 50*   *Helipad available*
Price Guide: *Single £70.00-£95.00*
                 Double £100.00-£140.00 (includes suites)
Location: *Direct route through Huntly - follow signs*
            for Huntly Castle then to Castle Hotel.

GLENGARRY CASTLE HOTEL

Invergarry, Inverness-shire. PH35 4HW
Tel: 01809 501254 Fax: 01809 501207
Email: castle@glengarry.net   www.glengarry.net

Glengarry Castle commands a stunning position overlooking Loch Oich between Loch Ness and Loch Lochy in this popular area of Scotland. The ruins of Invergarry Castle, the ancient seat of the McDonnells of Glengarry - which gave shelter to Bonnie Prince Charlie before and after the battle of Culloden stands within sight of the hotel. A real family castle hotel the MacCallum family have been here since 1958 and are rightly proud of their achievements - so many enjoyable visits/overnight stays over a number of years. This Victorian building with grand entrance hall has all the ingredients of that bygone era with large reception and public room areas all with views to the garden and loch. The 26 bedrooms, recently refurbished, have all the ensuite comforts one would expect, some with four posters. True highland hospitality here with fresh produce being the key to successful traditional cooking - the old fashioned afternoon teas a daily highlight. There are a number of activities to enjoy including walks through extensive woodlands, boating on the loch, fishing and making use of the newly surfaced Elastosol tennis court. Perfect stop over for those travelling to Skye or Inverness and beyond. Your host - Donald MacCallum.

Open: *Mar. 20th - Nov. 9th*	**Swimming Pool/Health Club:** *No*
No. Rooms: *26 En Suite 25*	**Conference Facilities:** *No*
Room telephones: *Yes*	**Price Guide:** *Single £62.00 - £82.00*
TV in Rooms: *Yes*	*Double £90.00 - £166.00*
Pets: *Yes* **Children:** *Yes*	**Location:** *One mile south of Invergarry on A82*
Disabled: *Limited*	*overlooking Loch Oich.*

AA

BUNCHREW HOUSE HOTEL

Bunchrew, Inverness. IV3 8TA

Tel: 01463 234917   Fax: 01463 710620

Email: welcome@bunchrewhousehotel.com   www.bunchrewhousehotel.com

This magnificent, well appointed 17th. century Scottish mansion is situated just outside Inverness on the shores of the Beauly Firth with breathtaking views of the Black Isle and Ben Wyvis to the north. It is surrounded by 20 acres of beautiful gardens and woodlands. This historic building attracts much interest and was originally built by the 8th. Lord Lovat in 1621. The extremely high standards I have come to know at Bunchrew House Hotel are maintained under the capable supervision of General Manager Gill Omand. Head chef Walter Walker takes great pride in providing traditional Scottish food - his expectations are high and there is a dedicated approach here which I have sampled myself. Well balanced combinations with clear and defined flavours. Accommodation consists of premium, superior and standard rooms, some with four poster beds and include all the 'extras'. Sister property, The Summer Isles Hotel (**Michelin star**) - see entry under Achiltibuie. Reservations for both through the one source if required. Both highly recommended.

Open: *All year (ex. Xmas)*	**Swimming Pool/Health Club:** *No*
No. Rooms: *16 En Suite 16*	**Conference Facilities:** *up to 80*
Room telephones: *Yes*	**Price Guide:** *Single from £110.00*
TV in Rooms: *Yes*	*Double from £160.00-£270.00*
Pets: *No* **Children:** *Yes*	**Location:** *3 miles outside city on A862 Beauly Road*
Disabled: *Yes*	

CULLODEN HOUSE HOTEL

Culloden, Inverness. IV2 7BZ
Tel: 01463 790461   Fax: 01463 792181
Email: info@cullodenhouse.co.uk   www.cullodenhouse.co.uk

Quite a majestic entrance to this property – a very stately mansion with all the 'trappings' of Bonnie Prince Charlie and the last battle on British soil in April 1746. The sweeping manicured lawns and building-clad virginia creeper cannot fail to impress the visitor and rightly so – the current 'Bonnie Prince Charlie' has been a visitor here of course. Within the elegance and charm of this hotel is true Highland hospitality – guests are met with a genuine welcome – there is a very friendly and relaxed atmosphere which immediately puts you at ease. Very 'hands on' approach from Stephen Davies the General Manager and his mother Pat over a number of years. Unfortunately, Pat is retiring in April 2010 and will be missed by all. Talented and devoted head chef Michael Simpson (23 years) is known by reputation for his culinary skills and holds the 2 AA red rosette award. Very impressed with the recent major refurbishment of the hotel - a complete change in furniture, carpets, drapes etc. This is not just a cosmetic exercise to fill in spaces. It is with the comfort of the guest in mind. The City of Inverness has itself a lot to offer the visitor – there are also a number of visitor and historical attractions in the area. Airport 15 minutes. Highly recommended.

Open: *All year*	**Swimming Pool/Health Club:** *No*
No. Rooms: *28 En Suite 28*	**Conference Facilities:** *Up to 40*
Room telephones: *Yes*	**Price Guide:** *Single £175.00-£365.00*
TV in Rooms: *Yes*	*Double £250.00-£375.00 (suite)*
Pets: *Yes* **Children:** *Yes*	*Enquire about seasonal breaks*
Disabled: *Not suitable*	**Location:** *3mls from Inverness & 3mls from airport*

AA ❀ ❀

THE KINGSMILLS

Culcabock Road, Inverness. IV2 3LP
Tel: 01463 237166   Fax: 01463 225208

Email: reservations@kingsmillshotel.com   www.kingsmillshotel.com

The Kingsmills will be remembered with great affection when it was in private hands. Over the years it was purchased by 'hotel chains' and the personal element disappeared. Now back in private hands there has been a massive improvement here – I was delighted to return after so many years. There is a major refurbishment programme to upgrade all bedrooms – I stayed in one of the superior bedrooms (lift to all floors) and it was extremely comfortable. Although the dining area is fairly large the attention to good service was obvious and staff even managed to maintain a personal touch which can be difficult. Enjoyed a really good dinner – simple combinations – uncomplicated and well executed. Very generous and comfortable public areas where you don't feel inhibited. Leisure facilities include a sizable swimming pool and gymnasium. Plans are in place to open another smaller hotel, the Kings Club, in the gounds of the main hotel. This will open in April 2010 and will offer the option of a modern contemporary choice of accomodation (37 bedrooms) and a luxury spa facility. It will also have its own food & beverage operation. Normally, I wouldn't include 'city hotels' in my book but this is an exception. Perfectly situated on the periphery of Inverness with ample car parking, it's good to see The Kingsmills in good hands once again. Your host and General Manager: Craig Ewan.

Open: *All year*	**Disabled:** *Yes*
No. Rooms: *77+*	**Swimming Pool/Health Club:** *Yes*
Room telephones: *Yes*	**Conference Facilities:** *Yes - 3 venues for up to 80*
TV in Rooms: *Yes*	**Price Guide:** *Double: £78.00 - £158.00*
Pets: *Yes*	**Location:** *Culcabock Road next to Inverness Golf course.*
Children: *Yes*	*1 mile from city centre.*

The finest wine glasses
for all your senses.

ROCPOOL RESERVE & CHEZ ROUX RESTAURANT

Culduthel Road, Inverness. IV2 4AG
Tel: 01463 240089   Fax: 01463 248431

Email: info@rocpool.com   www.rocpool.com   www.icmi.co.uk

Rocpool Reserve is quite unique and the first time in 15 years that a boutique hotel has appeared in my book. It is quite exceptional and snugly situated within a leafy suburb of Inverness. "Think of everything you know about hotels then forget it all instantly – Rocpool will redefine the experience for ever," are the opening words on the hotel brochure and having personally sampled the Rocpool experience I couldn't agree more. Luxurious bedrooms (some with hot tub) and bespoke soft furnishings are obvious. The theme throughout this hotel is all about quality whether it's the cuisine, accommodation, service or housekeeping. Known by reputation Albert Roux (see Food Foreword) has now brought his French influence to the kitchen at Rocpool. Dishes are French Country Classic with Albert using fresh produce from the immediate region. No complicated menu here – good choice and, I should add, at a very reasonable cost. Excellent wine cellar. Staff under the supervision of Kerry Watson will ensure a great stay at Rocpool. I have watched this hotel 'take shape' over a number of years. Now managed by Inverlochy Castle Management International. Uplift from Inverness airport for either hotel. Complete indulgence.

Open: *All year*	**Swimming Pool/Health Club:** *No*
No. Rooms: *11 En Suite 11*	**Conference Facilities:** *up to 20*
Room telephones: *Yes*	**Price Guide:** *Single £137.00-£156.00*
TV in Rooms: *Yes*	*Double £166.00-£356.00*
Pets: *No* **Children:** *Yes*	**Location:** *Make for Inverness Castle and proceed up*
Disabled: *Yes*	*Castle Street to Culduthel Road.*

For the last 50 years, MORTIMER'S OF GRANTOWN ON SPEY has supplied the best in fishing and outdoor leisure equipment to discerning sports men and women from all over the world.

We stock every conceivable quality accessory including the full range of Hardy fishing tackle and a vast range of equipment from other manufacturers. Most of the leading makes of outdoor clothing for men and women are stocked together with a full range of shooting accessories and ammunition. We even have our own Mortimer's range of single malt and blended whisky. Of course, supplying equipment is only part of our service to you. We are also able to supply fishing permits, from the Strathspey Angling Association, for both banks of a nearby 6 mile stretch of the River Spey. Tuition can be arranged with our experienced ghillies and with the use of the best tackle - hired from us!

We look forward to meeting you.

MORTIMER'S,
3 HIGH STREET,
GRANTOWN ON SPEY,
MORAY, PH26 3HB.
TEL: 01479 872684.
e-mail: mortimers@spey.fsnet.co.uk
www.mortimersofspeyside.co.uk

THE STEADINGS AT THE GROUSE & TROUT

Flichity, Farr, Inverness-shire. IV2 6XD
Tel: 01808 521314   Fax: 01808 521741
Email: stay@steadingshotel.co.uk   www.steadingshotel.co.uk

David & Mary Allen are to be congratulated on their achievements at this small hotel just south of Inverness on the A9 Fort Augustus road. (near Daviot) Formerly a farm steading circa 1860 it is now an extremely well restored and refurbished property. Care has been taken with the 9 en suite bedrooms – all refurbished to a high standard with extra touches. 2 bedroom 'cottages' attached to the hotel itself offer a slightly different option with access to the garden or the gazebo if you want a smoke! Gardens and surrounds are immaculate and the large conservatory looking out over the hills instills a sense of peace and contentment. Good wholesome cooking here (generous portions I should add) and I have never been disappointed. Service first class and a real friendly ambience prevails throughout. Game shooting/loch/river/sea fishing available locally. David & Mary extend a real warm welcome to all their guests and its really a 'home from home' atmosphere. Culloden battlefield just up the road – plenty to do and see or just take a wee stroll in the evening. Really good value for money. Favourite room 'Flichity' which is one of the 'cottage bedrooms'.

Open: *Mar-Dec.*	**Swimming Pool/Health Club:** *No*
No. Rooms: *9 En Suite*	**Conference Facilities:** *Up to 10*
Room telephones: *Yes* **TV in Rooms:** *Yes*	**Price Guide:** *Single £68.00*
Pets: *Yes (by arrangement)*	*Double from £95.00-£145.00*
Children: *Yes (by arrangement)*	**Location:** *Strathnairn between Farr & Croachy. 5mls*
Disabled: *Yes (dining only)*	*sth of Inverness take B851 to Ft. Augustus.*

Andrew Wilkie - Head Chef
Ballathie House

BALLATHIE HOUSE

Kinclaven, By Stanley, Perthshire. PH1 4QN
Tel: 01250 883268   Fax: 01250 883396
Email address: email@ballathiehousehotel.com   www.ballathiehousehotel.com

This is a magnificent property situated in its own country estate overlooking the River Tay noted for its fishing. The main driveway and garden policies in a woodland setting are immaculate. This house of character dates back to 1850 and is only a short drive from Perth. The main house has been upgraded – bedrooms and public areas all retain that elegance associated with a country house and offer every comfort. An option is the very sensitive development of the riverside rooms and suites with a short walk to the main building. Exceptional views over the Tay. A further option is the Sportsman's lodge rooms (en suite) and one self catering apartment. Award winning chef Andrew Wilkie performs 'miracles' in his kitchen and I have sampled his food here and before he arrived at Ballathie. No inconsistencies here – perfectly executed and diners expectations fully met. Ideal venue for weddings. Service and housekeeping could not be faulted. A lot of repeat business here which means once you have visited Ballathie House you will return. Your host Chris Longden. Highly recommended.

Open: *All year*	**Swimming Pool/Health Club:** *No*
No. Rooms: *42 En Suite 42*	**Conference Facilities:** *Boardroom meetings to 30*
Room telephones: *Yes*	**Price Guide:** *Single from £95.00 Double/Twin £190.00-£260.00*
TV in Rooms: *Yes*	*2 Day breaks from £99.00 P.P.P.N., D.B.B.*
Pets: *Yes* **Children:** *Yes*	**Location:** *Off A9, 2 miles North of Perth through Stanley/or*
Disabled: *Yes*	*off A93 at Beech hedge and signs.*

LYNNFIELD HOTEL & RESTAURANT

Holm Road, St, Ola, Kirkwall. KW15 1SU
Tel: 01856 872505
Email: office@lynnfield.co.uk www.lynnfieldhotel.com

Malcolm Stout and partner Lorna Reid are forging ahead with what can only be described as a great success story at The Lynnfield Hotel & Restaurant. Many will remember his years at Cleaton House on Westray which they ran very successfully – indeed also a VisitScotland 4 star property. Now relocated to Orkney mainland in 2006, their new premises the Lynnfield Hotel (next to the Highland Park Distillery) is a new challenge, but with careful planning they have developed and transformed this hotel to another 4 star VisitScotland status. 10 very luxurious bedrooms (including 1 disabled, 3 suites & 2 four posters) – offer every comfort. Their reputation for excellent Orcadian cuisine has followed from Westray, with daily evolving menus. Terrific view over the bay from the restaurant sets the tone for a wonderful dining experience. It's difficult sometimes for me to find a place of this quality in the islands of Scotland – on my visits to Orkney I always found there was plenty to do and see – I always need 3 days to cover visits to Skara Brae, the Ortak factory, the distillery and a wee drive over The Churchill Barriers. It is great to take an evening stroll into the town and do a bit of window shopping. Don't waste time – if you plan a trip to Orkney this is the place to stay – phone or email now.

Open: *All year*	**Swimming Pool/Health Club:** *No*
No. Rooms: *10 En Suite 10*	**Conference Facilities:** *Up to 30*
Room telephones:	**Price Guide:** *Single occupancy £85.00*
TV in Rooms: *Yes* **Pets:** *Arrangement*	*Double £110.00 - £150.00 (3 suites)*
Children: *Over 12*	**Location:** *A961 Holm Road where indicated.*
Disabled: *1 room*	*Near Highland Park Distillery*

THE FOUR SEASONS HOTEL
St. Fillans, Perthshire. PH6 2NF
Tel: 01764 685333 Fax: 01764 685444
www.thefourseasonshotel.co.uk

Aptly named for the ever changing weather patterns, this hotel has one of the finest lochside locations in Scotland. Its position looking south west down Loch Earn must be the envy of others set amongst scenic mountains and woodland. Snugly positioned at the west end of the village the panoramic views are magnificent. "With food to match" - quote from resident proprietor Andrew Low whose experience in culinary matters are not unknown. The major refurbishment a couple of years ago creates a wonderful ambience - a sophisticated oriental theme which mellows perfectly with other fabrics and decor - not overpowering and of a professional input. Dining in the Meal Reamhar restaurant or, less formally, in the Tarken Room is always a fine experience - well-balanced menus and cuisine of a distinctive high quality which sets the tone for the evening - finish the day with a good malt around the log fire. Bedrooms are spacious and comfortable - most overlook the loch - whilst 6 chalets at the rear of the hotel offer more privacy. Leisure activities are too numerous to mention. The hotel can provide first class facilities for small meetings or functions and Andrew holds a wedding licence for that special day. Good atmosphere here - 'laid back' as described in the hotel brochure. Good value for money. Please enquire about special breaks and the event weekends. (Also see front cover).

Open: *March - December inclusive*	**Swimming Pool/Health Club:** *No*
No. Rooms: *12 En Suite 12; 6 chalets*	**Conference Facilities:** *Up to 36*
Room telephones: *Yes*	**Price Guide:** *Single £55.00-£90.00*
TV in Rooms: *Yes*	*Double £88.00-£105.00*
Pets: *Yes* **Children:** *Yes*	*Chalets £44.00-£88-00*
Disabled: *No*	**Location:** *A85 - west end of St. Fillans village.*

GLENMORISTON ARMS HOTEL AND RESTAURANT

Invermoriston, by Loch Ness, Inverness-shire. IV63 7YA
Tel: 01320 351206   Fax: 01320 351308
Email: reception@glenmoristonarms.co.uk   www.glenmoristonarms.co.uk

Dating back to 1740, this former drovers inn is located in the heart of the village of Invermoriston just a short stroll from the world famous Loch Ness. It enjoys an excellent location situated on the crossroads of the gateway to Skye and the islands but also midway between Fort William and Inverness. This hotel is now back 'on track' with new owners Paul & Sue Hudson at the helm. Very much a 'hands on' operation. "Small is beautiful", as the saying goes - only 8 but extremely comfortable bedrooms - one a four poster. Excellent a la carte menu and the food & beverage operation here is really popular with the old residents lounge now catering for the 'overflow'. One thing that struck me was the great ambience within the hotel - friendly and very helpful. "The quintessential Scottish break everyone should have," remarked a guest - such is the ambience of the hotel. The Moriston Bar now contains over 140 single malt whiskies plus a very extensive and sophisticated wine list. Excellent value for money.

Open: *All year except Jan & Feb*	**Swimming Pool/Health Club:** *No*	
No. Rooms: *8 En Suite 8*	**Conference Facilities:** *No*	
Room telephones: *Yes*	**Price Guide:** *Single £75.00 Double £120.00-£150.00*	
TV in Rooms: *Yes*	*Four Poster £150.00*	
Pets: *No* **Children:** *Yes*	**Location:** *Midway between Inverness and Fort William on*	
Disabled: *Dining only*	*A82 - hotel in village of Invermoriston*	

THE BUCCLEUCH ARMS HOTEL
High Street, Moffat, Dumfries. DG10 9ET
Tel: 01683 220003   Fax: 01683 221291
Email: enquiries@buccleucharmshotel.com   www.buccleucharmshotel.com

In my view this is the only hotel in Moffat which I can endorse and include in my book. With constant re-investment and a lot of hard work, the Smith family have taken this hotel to a new level - if you ask anyone in the area where they would eat out, it is always The Buccleuch Arms. Executive chef Lara Smith supervises menus and dishes which clearly indicate a dedication and knowledge of the industry. Quality sourcing of ingredients from this rich agricultural area of Scotland and some from further afield. Culinary skills do the rest. The upstairs dining room creates the perfect ambience. Bedrooms are en suite and offer every comfort – downstairs the lounge/bar area is ideal for the pre-dinner apertif and a good 'blether'. Staff (training here is obvious) treat guests with courtesy and at all times are extremely attentive and helpful. Customer expectations are fully met. Come and relax at this famous border town – lots to see and do – excellent value for money. Very active members of the Scotch Beef Club and winner of the Gold award for Green Tourism.

Open: *All year*	**Disabled**: *No*
No. Rooms: *18 En Suite 18*	**Swimming Pool/Health Club:** *No*
Room telephones: *By request*	**Conference Facilities:** *Up to 60*
TV in Rooms: *Yes*	**Price Guide:** *Single from £50.00*
Pets: *Yes*	*Double from £80.00*
Children: *Yes*	**Location:** *Moffat - High Street*

THE GOLF VIEW HOTEL

Seabank Road, Nairn. IV12 4HD

Tel: 01667 452301 Fax: 01667 455267

Email: sales.golfview@crerarmanagement.com www.swallow-hotels.com

Getting back 'on the radar' again since Crerar Hotels took over and installed an experienced management team. This well known hotel in Nairn is situated at the seafront with magnificent views over the Moray Firth. Enjoyed my overnight stay here this year. So much potential with 42 spacious bedrooms – option of 4 poster with spa, family or adjoining rooms, rooms suiting couples or individuals. Lift to all floors. Leisure facilities include swimming pool, gym, spa bath, sauna & steam room – ladies can make use of beauty treatment on offer in the hotel salon. Food served in the conservatory or the dining room – fresh produce and sound quality produces simple uncomplicated dishes. Perfect venue for corporate meetings – set-up for 120 delegates and the hotel holds a wedding and civil ceremony licence. Now if you are a golfer – 25 courses I am told within a short distance of the hotel! Culloden battlefield, Cawdor Castle & Dunrobin Castle just a few of the interesting places to visit. City of Inverness – 14 miles.

Open: *All year*	**Swimming Pool/Health Club:** *Yes*
No. Rooms: *42 en suite*	**Conference Facilities:** *up to 120*
Room telephones: *Yes*	**Price Guide:** *Single £70.00 - £90.00*
TV in Rooms: *Yes*	*Double £80.00 - £170.00 (suite)*
Pets: *Yes* **Children:** *Yes*	**Location:** *From A96 into Seabank Rd at Parish church in Nairn*
Disabled: *Yes with lift*	*- drive to sea - on right hand side at bottom of road*

AA

KIRROUGHTREE HOUSE

Newton Stewart, Wigtownshire DG8 6AN
Tel: 01671 402141 Fax: 01671 402425
Email: info@kirroughtreehouse.co.uk www.kirroughtreehouse.co.uk

No doubt one of my favourites in the south west of Scotland with a great core of loyal customers who return year after year. The drive up to the hotel encompasses 8 acres of landscaped gardens which are magnificent, more so when the 'rhodies' are in bloom. This unusual building has been carefully restored and refurbished in keeping with the original house with varying degrees of comfort – from standard, de luxe and the opulent regal suite. All are elegant in their own right – my own room (downstairs) with entrance/exit from the rear and lift to ground floor, was massive. The ensuite facility was as large as a bedroom! The elegant theme continues through to the wood-panelled, extremely comfortable lounge (where you order dinner) and the 2 dining rooms. Had a chat with Rolf Mueller, head chef, who produced a first class dining experience – so consistent over the years he works miracles in the kitchen. Menus short but creative – obviously good prep work here. Great ambience throughout. Service very professional and friendly. Good base for exploring the delights of the south west. Your host: Jim Stirling (who deserves a long service medal!)

Open: *Feb 14-Jan 3*	**Swimming Pool/Health Club:** *No*	
No. Rooms: *17 En Suite 17*	**Conference Facilities:** *Max 20*	
Room telephones: *Yes*	**Price Guide:**	*Single £90.00-£125.00*
TV in Rooms: *Yes*		*Double £180.00-£250.00*
Pets: *By arrangement* **Children:** *Over 10*	**Location:**	*From A75 take A712 New Galloway*
Disabled: *Limited*		*Road. Hotel 300 yards on left.*

THE MANOR HOUSE

Gallanach Road, Oban, Argyll. PA34 4LS
Tel: 01631 562087   Fax: 01631 563053
Email: info@manorhouseoban.com   www.manorhouseoban.com

On the outskirts of Oban just beyond the ferry terminal this Georgian House, built in 1780 commands an enviable position overlooking the Oban bay to the islands beyond. Known to me for many years it is situated in a quiet spot away from the main centre of Oban and retains the charm and elegance of a bygone era. Under the personal supervision of General Manager Gregor MacKinnon, this small hotel offers every comfort one would expect from a VisitScotland 4 star rating and cuisine to match. Bedrooms are extremely comfortable (some with views over the bay), public rooms are spacious, well furnished and cosy with log fire in the winter (when I stayed). The restaurant is a delight under the personal supervision of talented chef Patrick Freytag – well known for its use of fresh local produce. Fresh fish (as one would expect) lamb and game in season could be your choice. Ideal stay for a day journey to the island of Mull or explore the beautiful Argyll coastland north or south of Oban. Breath-taking views from many points along the way. AA one rosette for food. A favourite with many over the years.

Open: *All year except Christmas*	**Swimming Pool/Health Club:** *No*
No. Rooms: *11 En Suite 11*	**Conference Facilities:** *No*
Room telephones: *Yes*	**Price Guide:** *Single £120.00 – £185.00 (includes dinner)*
TV in Rooms: *Yes*	*Double £163.00 – £245.00 (includes dinner)*
Pets: *By request* **Children:** *Over 12*	*Enquire about seasonal breaks.*
Disabled: *Restricted*	**Location:** *200yds past ferry terminal on Gallanach Road.*

Scottish TOURIST BOARD ★★★★ RESTAURANT WITH ROOMS   **AA**

HEBRIDEAN PRINCESS

Kintail House, Skipton, N. Yorks. BD23 2DE
Tel: 01756 704704   Fax: 01756 704734
Email: reservations@hebridean.co.uk   www.hebridean.co.uk

Sailing mainly from Oban and Fairlie, experience the most beautiful scenery of the British Isles aboard the luxurious Hebridean Princess. This small and unique cruise ship with immaculately maintained teak decks and polished brass, cruises through the Western Isles of Scotland and across the Irish Sea in inimitable style. The epitome of understated elegance, from the panoramic Tiree Lounge to the plush Columba Restaurant, the public rooms and 30 spacious cabins are beautifully designed and decorated throughout. Imaginative menus are created using the freshest local produce to bring you memorable breakfasts and elegant dining, with first class service from one of the best crews afloat. Hebridean Princess sails Scotland's Western Isles between March and November, with a maximum of 49 guests. During 20 seasons she has explored some of Scotland's most remote regions, sailing as far west as far flung St Kilda, and north to the Orkneys, Shetlands and Norway. In her 2010 programme she will visit Northern Ireland, the Isle of Man and the Northern Isles.

Open: *March to November*	**Swimming Pool/Health Club:** *No*
No. Cabins: *30 En Suite 30*	**Conference Facilities:** *No*
TV in Rooms: *Yes*	**Price Guide:** *5 night cruise: from £986.00 per person*
Pets: *No*	*7 night cruise: from £1547.00 per person*
Children: *Aged 9 and over*	*(both based on 2 sharing a double cabin)*
Disabled: *Unsuitable*	**Location:** *Sails from Oban*

CRINGLETIE HOUSE

Peebles, Peeblesshire. EH45 8PL
Tel: 01721 725750 Fax: 01721 725751
Email: enquiries@cringletie.com www.cringletie.com

This is one of the finest country houses in the country – a labour of love by the owners Johanna & Jacob van Houdt has restored this fine baronial property to its former glories. Located and perfectly signposted it is positioned just off the main Edinburgh-Peebles road in woodland and well attended gardens – the 400 year walled garden worth a visit on its own. Panoramic views to hill & glen. There are 12 individually decorated bedrooms (sampled by myself on 2 occasions) and 1 suite – modern amenities are very 'high tech'. Spacious with superior en suite facilities that just exude comfort. Also an excellent room on the ground floor for the disabled. Modern lift to other levels of the house is a real bonus. Great ambience in the restaurant on the first floor. Superior furnishings and drapes sets the tone. Cuisine of an AA 2 rosette standard allied with first class front of house service – friendly staff, neatly uniformed and not too formal. There is also a designated dining room for private parties and I enjoy a conservatory lunch quite often when I visit here. Ideal venue for weddings (on an exclusive basis) and a corporate meeting away from the city centre. Just indulge yourself – a good malt after dinner, a walk in the grounds or whatever – wonderful experience. 4 AA red stars. VisitScotland award: 4 gold stars.

Open: *Closed 3rd-27th January*	**Swimming Pool/Health Club:** *No*
No. Rooms: *12 + 1 suite*	**Conference Facilities:** *50-60*
Room telephones: *Yes*	**Price Guide:** *Single from £165.00 for standard room*
TV in Rooms: *Yes*	*Double from £115.00 for standard room (pppn)*
Pets: *Yes* **Children:** *Yes*	*DBB available + seasonal breaks*
Disabled: *Yes - 1 room*	**Location:** *From Peebles take A703 north – 2 miles on left.*

Scottish TOURIST BOARD ★★★★ COUNTRY HOUSE HOTEL GOLD

AA❀❀ ★★★★

THE SCOTCH BEEF CLUB

POOL HOUSE

Poolewe, By Achnasheen, Wester Ross. IV22 2LD
Tel: 01445 781272 Fax: 01445 781403
Email: stay@pool-house.co.uk www.pool-house.co.uk

A stunning property on the shores of Loch Ewe with panoramic views within a brief walk of the famous Inverewe gardens. It could also be described as a romantic haven. As from October 31st Pool House will operate under the banner of Guest Accommodation 5 star with a similar award from the AA. This does not detract in any way from the pure indulgence of staying at Pool House. All bedrooms just exude opulence – spacious with quality furnishings and really nice touches. Magnificent, large en suite bathrooms. I have stayed here on several occasions and often fall asleep in front of the roaring fire in the lounge. Complete relaxation. Open decking with hot tub if requested. Or have a game of billiards, read a book or take a stroll in the evening. The food & beverage operation has changed slightly but you won't go hungry! Head chef John Moir (known to me personally) will provide fine dining on at least 2 nights with light meals on others days, eg. seafood platter etc. Closed on Mondays. Peter, Margaret, Elizabeth & Mhairi Harrison are the perfect hosts in this wonderful setting in Wester Ross. Ideal property for exclusive use (catering would be organised). Price guide has changed to reflect the changes with a minimum of a 2 night stay. In my view not long enough. Highly recommended.

Open: *Closed Mondays only*	**Swimming Pool/Health Club:** *No*
No. Rooms: *4 Suites; 1 single; 1 double*	**Conference Facilities:** *No*
Room telephones: *Yes*	**Price Guide:** *Single £110.00 Double £190.00 (all suites)*
TV in Rooms: *Yes*	*Dinner £45.00*
Pets: *No* **Children:** *Over 16*	*Seasonal breaks available*
Disabled: *Limited*	**Location:** *Next to Inverewe Gardens.*

Scottish
TOURIST BOARD
★★★★★
ACCOMMODATION

PARK LODGE HOTEL

32 Park Terrace, Stirling FK8 2JS
Tel: 01786 474862 Fax: 01786 449748
Email: info@parklodge.net www.parklodge.net

This is a fine Georgian mansion with walled garden situated in a delightful part of the town overlooking Stirling Castle. There are also fine views of the Campsie Fell hills and beyond. The furnishings are luxurious and reflect an era of gracious elegance. The bedrooms (some with 4 poster) are a delight – all en suite and again in the mould of a past era. The cuisine here is excellent - the culinary skills of French chef Georges Marquetty and his son Jean Pierre should be recognised but Georges is modest about his achievements but well known to his faithful followers. Anne Marquetty on hand to assure you of a warm welcome - known this family for twenty years now and can thoroughly recommend a stay over in Stirling at this establishment. There is a well stocked cocktail bar with a wide range of malt whiskies – tempting in itself after a splendid meal. There is so much of Scotland's heritage here in Stirling to see and visit. The film 'Braveheart' highlighted the story of Sir William Wallace and the famous battle of Stirling Bridge in 1297. Only 15 minutes walk to the centre of the town.

Open: *All year*	**Swimming Pool/Health Club:** *No*
No. Rooms: *10 En Suite 10*	**Conference Facilities:** *Up to 50, functions up to 150*
Room telephones: *Yes*	**Price Guide:** *Single from £70.00 Double from £100.00*
TV in Rooms: *Yes*	*Suite: £150.00*
Pets: *Yes* **Children:** *Yes*	**Location:** *Opposite golf course in King's Park.*
Disabled: *Yes*	

DRYBURGH ABBEY HOTEL

St. Boswells, Melrose, Roxburghshire. TD6 0RQ
Tel: 01835 822261 Fax: 01835 823945
Email: enquiries@dryburgh.co.uk www.dryburgh.co.uk

Nestling in a magnificent wooded private estate on the banks of the River Tweed and immediately adjacent to the historic Dryburgh Abbey, Dryburgh Abbey Hotel commands a stunning position with magnificent views in the heart of the borders. This Scottish baronial mansion dates from the 19th century. Superior bedrooms are spacious, attractively decorated with every comfort one would expect and nice 'extra touches' - some with panoramic views. Great improvement in the food & beverage operation since Mark Greenaway was appointed head chef. A dedicated approach with high technical skills and great judgement in combining and balancing ingredients. This ambition has now been recognised with the addition of another AA rosette for food. Meals can be taken informally in the lounge or bar area or more formally in the Tweed Restaurant on the first floor. Don't forget the indoor pool - ideal after a day filled with walking, fishing, touring, sporting or just relaxing by the pool itself. Sir Walter Scott's name is synonomous with this part of the Scottish borders – also renowned for its agriculture and rugby! Ideal venue for corporate matters ('away from it all') or weddings - just an hour's drive down the A68 from Edinburgh. Your hosts: John and Mark Wallace.

Open: *All year*	**Disabled:** *Yes*
No. Rooms: *38 (all En Suite)*	**Swimming Pool/Sauna:** *Yes*
Room telephones: *Yes*	**Conference Facilities:** *Yes*
TV in Rooms: *Yes*	**Price Guide:** *£65-£175 (Lady of Mertoun Suite) p.p.p.n.*
Pets: *Yes*	*Enquire about seasonal breaks*
Children: *Yes*	**Location:** *2 miles from St. Boswells, Scottish Borders.*

Scottish TOURIST BOARD ★★★★ COUNTRY HOUSE HOTEL

AA ✿ ✿

FORSS HOUSE HOTEL

Forss, By Thurso, Caithness. KW14 7XY
Tel: 01847 861201 Fax: 01847 861301
Email: anne@forsshousehotel.co.uk www.forsshousehotel.co.uk

Forss House nestles in 20 acres of woodland beside a picturesque water mill just 4 miles outside Thurso Once again a very enjoyable stay at Forss House. The investment and improvements over the last 5 years have been impressive when it was purchased by the owners of the internationally-renowned Ackergill Tower near Wick. Stayed here over a 12 year period and have witnessed the progress made at this property. All main hotel bedrooms have been refurbished to an extremely high standard – obviously, a professional input that is evident with the quality of furnishings and fabrics. Large en suite bathrooms a delight. There are 4 de-luxe apartments within the grounds of the hotel - suit the slightly disabled with parking at your front door. Seasonal menus and culinary skills present an excellent dinner – noticed the service was impeccable and friendly and that there was a great ambience from the pre-dinner drink through to the coffee. Cocktail bar boasts over 300 malts and there is a function suite that can take up to 16 for private dinners etc. Gillsbay ferry to Orkney is 'just down the road' as is John O' Groats and Castle of Mey, Plenty to do here – stay a bit longer this time and enjoy. Your host (and what a lovely character!): Anne Mackenzie.

Open: *All year (closed 23rd Dec – 4th Jan)*	**Disabled:** *Limited*
No. Rooms: *14 En Suite 14*	**Swimming Pool/Health Club:** *No*
Room telephones: *Yes*	**Conference Facilities:** *Up to 20*
TV in Rooms: *Yes*	**Price Guide:** *Single from £95.00-£110.00*
Pets: *Yes*	*Double from £125.00-£160.00*
Children: *Yes*	**Location:** *4 miles from Thurso on A836*

AA ❀ ❀

TIRORAN HOUSE HOTEL

Tiroran, Isle of Mull, Argyll. PA69 6ES
Tel: 01681 705232

Email: info@tiroran.com   www.tiroran.com

If you are going to Mull this is certainly the place to stay – absolutely stunning loch side views and property. The gardens are truly magnificent with well manicured lawns overlooking Loch Scridain. A real paradise. I discovered Tiroran 19 years ago and was delighted to return. Situated 4 miles off the 'main road' on the south part of the island it's a short hop to Iona and trips to Staffa. Laurence & Katie Mackay arrived here in 2004 and describe Tiroran as a boutique hotel – ideal for that discerning visitor – bedrooms are just so comfortable (king size beds) with a lot of extra touches and extremely well furnished. Excellent en suite facilities. Pre-dinner drinks with Laurence in the lounge sets the tone in the evening. Cuisine 'a la Katie' was a real experience – good use of fresh produce – some from loch to table. Organic garden. Dedication here and a real effort with the comfort of the guest in mind. Although a hotel, it's really a charming home with terrific ambience. There are 3 self catering units on the property. Usually a minimum of a 2 night stay but you will require more time to explore the island of Mull. Places of interest are Duart Castle (home of the clan MacLean) Torosay Gardens and of course a visit to Tobermory.

Open: *All year*	**Swimming Pool/Health Club:** *No*	
No. Rooms: *8 En Suite 8*	**Conference Facilities:** *No*	
Room telephones: *Yes*	**Price Guide:** *Single from £125.00 Double £135.00-£175.00*	
TV in Rooms: *Yes*		*King size and superking beds (also twins) available*
Pets: *Arrangement* **Children:** *Over 12*	**Location:**	*Craignure-Iona ferry road south. Turn off at*
Disabled: *Limited*		*Kinloch onto the B8035 for 4 miles.*

The King and I

THE TORRIDON

Torridon, Wester Ross IV22 2EY
Tel: 01445 791242 Fax: 01445 712253
Email: info@thetorridon.com www.thetorridon.com

The approach to The Torridon whether from Kyle of Lochalsh or Kinlochewe is quite magnificent, but keep your eyes on the single track roads! The hotel nestles in woodland surrounded by mountains and loch. Impressive driveway with manicured lawns and you already feel that this is a haven of peace and contentment. Formerly built in 1887 it was the home of the Earl of Lovelace and was a Victorian shooting lodge in the grand style of the day. Now operated by Rohaise and Daniel Rose-Bristow. The laid-back style of a bygone era has been retained here and this is a well run operation. Bedrooms in the main hotel are all very spacious – large king size beds with all modern amenities – some with magnificent views. Large en suite bathrooms which complement the rooms. Award-winning chef Kevin Broome performs miracles in his kitchen – he has been here for 7 years now and a very solid 2 AA rosette chef. In addition, and within the grounds, the Torridon Inn is available with family rooms for up to 6 people where you can dine informally in a Bistro style. The new luxury 2 bedroomed Boat House is a must for the romantic – with its own private road and jetty. Known as an activity destination it can provide anything from archery to falconry plus all the main physical activities (mountain & glen). Please note, rates vary on season and length of stay.

Open: *All year ex. 4 weeks January*	**Swimming Pool/Health Club:** *No*
No. Rooms: *19 En Suite 19*	**Conference Facilities:** *16 Director level*
Room telephones: *Yes*	**Price Guide:** *Single £130.00 +*
TV in Rooms: *Yes*	*Double £140.00-£395.00 (master room rates)*
Pets: *Yes - in cottage* **Children:** *Yes*	**Location:** *Inverness - Achnasheen. Take A832 to Kinlochewe*
Disabled: *Yes*	*village. Take turning clearly marked Torridon 10 miles.*

Scottish TOURIST BOARD ★★★★ COUNTRY HOUSE HOTEL GOLD

AA❀❀ ★★★★

Barry Quinion - Head Chef
Farlam Hall

FARLAM HALL

Brampton, Cumbria. CA8 2NG
Tel: 016977 46234   Fax: 016977 46683

Email: farlam@relaischateaux.com   www.farlamhall.co.uk

This is truly a magnificent 17th century ivy clad country manor set amongst wonderful parkland – a member of the prestigious Relais & Chateaux no less. The lake and fountain to the front are remarkable features – from the moment you arrive and enter Farlam Hall there is an atmosphere of peace and contentment. A stroll in the gardens with afternoon tea sets the tone –   bedrooms are extremely comfortable – spacious (large windows) and well furnished complimented by large en suite bathrooms. Recent upgrading entailed bathroom tiling with underneath floor heating and many yards of new carpeting which maintains the elegance of Farlam Hall. The Quinion and Stevenson families have owned Farlam Hall since 1975 and the finest traditions of hotel keeping are evident. The comfort of the guest is paramount. Add to this the fine cuisine and attentive service and you have the complete product. Daily-changing menus - a great dining experience. All fresh ingredients, carefully sourced and so well executed by chef Barry Quinion. Home made desserts 'to die for'. Just 'over the border' this is an ideal stop whether travelling north or south. Hadrian's Wall and many other historical sites closeby. Go for it, indulge yourself. Enjoyed my stay again this year and will return. 3 AA red stars.

Open: *All year ex. 24th - 31st Dec*	**Swimming Pool/Health Club:** *No*
No. Rooms: *12 En Suite 12*	**Conference Facilities:** *Up to 12 director level*
Room telephones: *Yes*	**Price Guide:** *Single £155.00-£175.00*
TV in Rooms: *Yes*	*Double £290.00-£330.00*
Pets: *Yes* **Children:** *Over 5*	**Location:** *Junction 43 on M6. 12 miles on A689 to*
Disabled: *Not suitable*	*Alston. Not in Farlam village.*

MALLORY COURT HOTEL

Harbury Lane, Leamington Spa, Warwickshire. CV33 9QB
Tel: 01926 330214   Fax: 01926 415714
email: reception@mallory.co.uk   www.mallory.co.uk

Mallory Court Hotel is a breathtakingly beautiful country house hotel, set in 10 acres of gardens and just outside Leamington Spa, Warwickshire. One of the AA's top 200 hotels in the UK & Ireland, Mallory is the only establishment in Warwickshire to be awarded a **Michelin star** and has retained the prestigious accolade for many years. The Michelin rated hotel already holds 3 AA rosettes for the main Dining Room but now the Brasserie at Mallory has been recognised by the AA with the award of 1 rosette. This elegant, Lutens-style country manor house is quite the little piece of England; an idyllic, impeccable retreat set in 10 acres of landscaped grounds and immaculate lawns. Contemporary country house splendour is the style, where pampered relaxation comes easy in sumptuous lounges over aperitifs or coffee, the mellow, homely atmosphere cultivated by an efficient, dedicated and enthusiastic team.

Open: *All year*	**Disabled:** *1 room designated (lift access)*
No. Rooms: *30*	**Swimming Pool/Health Club:** *Yes*
Room telephones: *Yes*	**Conference Facilities:** *Excellent - up to 160*
TV in Rooms: *Yes*	**Price Guide:** *£125.00-£395.00*
Pets: *arrangement*	**Location:** *M40 from London, Jct. 13; from Birmingham*
Children: *Yes*	*Jct. 14. 2 mls. on B4087 to Leamington Spa.*

AA ❀❀❀

★★★

MARLFIELD HOUSE

Gorey, Co. Wexford, Ireland.
Tel: (00353) 5394 21124   Fax: (00353) 5394 21572
Email: info@marlfieldhouse.ie   www.marlfieldhouse.com

Once again I am delighted to include Marlfield House as my Irish 'Associate Hotel' for edition 2010. It came strongly recommended and is a member of the prestigious Relais & Chateaux group. Formerly the residence of the Earls of Courtown Marlfield House is a very elegant 19th. century mansion set in its own grounds of wonderful garden, woodland and parkland policies. The State Rooms are decorated with rich fabrics and fine antique furniture - all have period marble fireplaces and elegant marble bathrooms. Every room is spacious and offers every luxury. The interior of the hotel is resplendent with fine paintings and antiques and the conservatory is a feature overlooking the garden. Cuisine described as 'classical with a French and Mediterranean influence' which has been awarded 3 AA red rosettes for food. The Bowe family are to be congratulated on keeping the standards of yesterday today. To maintain such high standards is testament to a firm commitment and dedication. Relais & Chateaux member since 1984. 3 AA red stars. General Managers: Margaret and Laura Bowe.

Open: *All year exc. Jan 2nd - mid Feb.*	**Disabled:** *Limited*
No. Rooms: *13 (6 suites) En Suite 13*	**Swimming Pool/Health Club:** *No*
Room telephones: *Yes*	**Conference Facilities:** *Small - Director Level*
TV in Rooms: *Yes*	**Price Guide:** *Double. Room - Standard:* **Euro 260-295**
Pets: *Arrangement*	*State Rooms:* **Euro 405-790 (Master)**
Children: *Yes*	**Location:** *80 km south of Dublin*

AA ❀❀❀
★★★

YNYSHIR HALL

Eglwysfach, Machynlleth, Powys, SY20 8TA

Tel: 01654 781209   Fax: 01654 781366

email: info@ynyshir-hall.co.uk   www.ynyshir-hall.co.uk

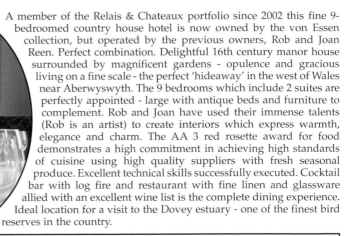

A member of the Relais & Chateaux portfolio since 2002 this fine 9-bedroomed country house hotel is now owned by the von Essen collection, but operated by the previous owners, Rob and Joan Reen. Perfect combination. Delightful 16th century manor house surrounded by magnificent gardens - opulence and gracious living on a fine scale - the perfect 'hideaway' in the west of Wales near Aberwyswyth. The 9 bedrooms which include 2 suites are perfectly appointed - large with antique beds and furniture to complement. Rob and Joan have used their immense talents (Rob is an artist) to create interiors which express warmth, elegance and charm. The AA 3 red rosette award for food demonstrates a high commitment in achieving high standards of cuisine using high quality suppliers with fresh seasonal produce. Excellent technical skills successfully executed. Cocktail bar with log fire and restaurant with fine linen and glassware allied with an excellent wine list is the complete dining experience. Ideal location for a visit to the Dovey estuary - one of the finest bird reserves in the country.

Open: *All year*	**Disabled:** *1 room*
No. Rooms: *9 (2 suites) En Suite 9*	**Swimming Pool/Health Club:** *No*
Room telephones: *Yes*	**Conference Facilities:** *Director level 25*
TV in Rooms: *Yes*	**Price Guide:** *Double £250.00-£305.00*
Pets: *1 room only*	*Suites £285.00 - £405.00*
Children: *Over 9*	**Location:** *10 miles from Aberwystwyth.*

AA❀ ❀ ❀
★★★

STEVENSONS

SCOTLAND'S
GOOD FOOD BOOK WITH RECIPES
2010

Photo by kind permission of Rocpool Reserve, Inverness

STEVENSONS

SCOTLAND'S
GOOD FOOD BOOK
2010

FOREWORD

Inverness, the Capital of the Highlands was a small town I first visited with my family many years ago to indulge in a favourite pass time of mine, fishing. That small town has now been Europe's fastest growing city for the last several years and I am delighted and excited to have opened my first Scottish restaurant Chez Roux here.

My relationship with Rocpool Reserve started about 5 years ago with their sister hotel the award winning 5 star Inverlochy Castle Hotel by Fort William in the west coast of Scotland. Inverlochy's kitchen has had a Michelin Star for numerous years and I was delighted to work along with their chefs in creating and hosting 'Gourmet Weekends'.

In March 2008, Inverlochy decided to purchase a boutique hotel in Inverness, 64 miles North of Inverlochy. I was invited up to have a look and quite honestly I had never seen anything like this outside London and was therefore keen to develop my relationship with Inverlochy to Rocpool Reserve, and the result is Chez Roux.

Concentrating on the kind of food I grew up with and loved combined with quality local produce, we created a menu with a classic French country feel to it. Basically letting the ingredients themselves do the talking with the emphasis being on the produce used and value for money. I have introduced some classic dishes from Le Gavroche like my Gruyere Cheese Soufflé and Pike Quenelle, which prove to be a favourite time and time again.

Inverlochy has been in the Stevensons Guide for the last 14 years and it was a natural choice for Rocpool Reserve and Chez Roux to choose when deciding on what guides to publish in. We look forward to welcoming you to my first Scottish restaurant.

Albert Roux
Rocpool Reserve, Inverness, IV2 4AG
Tel: 01463 240089 info@rocpool.com www.rocpool.com

Albert Henri Roux O.B.E.
Rocpool Reserve, Inverness

GLENKINDIE ARMS

Glenkindie, Alford, Aberdeenshire. AB33 8SX

Tel: 019756 41288

Email: iansimpson1873@live.co.uk www.theglenkindiearmshotel.com

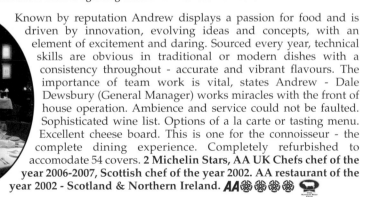

A fantastic country inn tucked away in an isolated part of Strathdon not far from Alford. A former drovers inn, it still has the aura of a bygone era situated amongst woodland in an attractive rural setting. Ian Simpson and his partner Aneta have only been here a short time and have 'set the heather alight' with food, expertly sourced and prepared. Ian, a highly skilled chef is absolutely motivated and dedicated to his task with Aneta working the front of house. Already extremely popular with the local fraternity he is now drawing customers from Aberdeen & Inverness. Recently awarded an AA rosette for food. James Chassels, who did the overnight stay for me described the food as, "rustic-with well sourced ingredients and no-nonsense style of cooking bringing out the best of flavours." Blackboard and bistro menu offering a good selection. Traditional Sunday roast a winner at £14:00. (3 course) Moderate wine list but a good cask of real ale here. Maybe not fine dining as we know it but don't be deceived – this is really excellent fayre in a typical country environment. There are 3 comfortable bedrooms. **AA**

Open: *All year*	**Disabled:** *Dining only*	**Covers:**	28
No Rooms: *3*	**Price Guide:** *£40.00 - £60.00 (Room)*		
TV in Rooms: *Yes*	*Lunch: from £10.00*		
Room Tel. *No*	*Dinner: from £12.50*		
Children: *Yes*	**Location:** *A97 from Alford just beyond Kildrummy.*		

ANDREW FAIRLIE@GLENEAGLES

The Gleneagles Hotel, Auchterarder, Perthshire. PH3 1NF

Tel: 01764 694267 Fax: 01764 694163.

Email: andrew.fairlie@gleneagles.com www.andrewfairlie.com

Known by reputation Andrew displays a passion for food and is driven by innovation, evolving ideas and concepts, with an element of excitement and daring. Sourced every year, technical skills are obvious in traditional or modern dishes with a consistency throughout - accurate and vibrant flavours. The importance of team work is vital, states Andrew - Dale Dewsbury (General Manager) works miracles with the front of house operation. Ambience and service could not be faulted. Sophisticated wine list. Options of a la carte or tasting menu. Excellent cheese board. This is one for the connoisseur - the complete dining experience. Completely refurbished to accomodate 54 covers. **2 Michelin Stars, AA UK Chefs chef of the year 2006-2007, Scottish chef of the year 2002. AA restaurant of the year 2002 - Scotland & Northern Ireland. AA**

Open: *All year (Dinner only) ex 3wks Jan. Closed Sun.*	**Disabled:** *Unsuitable*		
No Rooms: *N/A*	**Covers:** *54*		
TV in Rooms: *N/A*	**Price Guide:** *£75.00 - £95.00*		
Room Tel. *N/A*	*Cheese £14.00 Coffee £5.00*		
Children: *Over 12*	**Location:** *Ground floor of Gleneagles Hotel.*		

BOATH HOUSE
Auldearn, Nairn. IV12 5TE
Tel: 01667 454896

Email: info@boath-house.com   www.boath-house.com

This has been 'home' to head chef Charlie Lockley for the past 12 years. He spent his 'apprenticeship' under the watchful eye of J. Gordon Macintyre at Clifton House in Nairn (now a private residence). No compromise here – cuisine which demonstrates a thorough grounding in classical techniques and equally at ease with modern or traditional dishes. Innovation with an element of excitement and all items made in house. Knows all his suppliers on a personal basis and only quality ingredients are used – foraged food such as herbs, fruit, wild garlic and chanterelles are mandatory. Superior wine cellar to complement a fine dining experience – perfectly executed. Dining room overlooking the vast lawn expertly tabled with fine linen. Front of house staff show that professional attitude – efficient but extremely friendly. The award of 4 AA rosettes and a **Michelin Star** is true testament to a lot of hard work by Charlie Lockley and his kitchen brigade. Your hosts: Don & Wendy Matheson. **AA**🏵🏵🏵🏵 ●

Open: *All year*		**Covers:**	*28*
No Rooms: *8*		**Price Guide:**	*Dinner: £65.00 (6 courses)*
TV in Rooms: *Yes*	**Room Tel.** *Yes*		*Lunch: £28.50 (3 courses)*
Children: *Yes*		**Location:**	*1 mile east of Nairn on main Inverness-*
Disabled: *1 Room*			*Aberdeen road.*

BRAIDWOODS
Drumastle Mill Cottage, By Dalry, Ayrshire, KA24 4LN.
Tel: 01294 833544 Fax: 01294 833553

email: keithbraidwood@btconnect.com www.braidwoods.co.uk

I knew Keith Braidwood when he was making a name for himself at Shieldhill Castle near Biggar. Part of his earlier years were spent at Inverlochy Castle in the highlands. Always with the idea that he wanted his own restaurant he chose a country cottage just outside Dalry which conveys a distinct feeling of being 'in the middle of nowhere' surrounded by fields. Perfect. I have sampled Keith's culinary skills - by repute expectations of the kitchen are high and I was not disappointed. High technical skills here with flair and a consistency throughout the meal - depth and flavour evident. Restricted menu? Not so - balanced menus (lunch & dinner) offer excellent choice. Whole roast boneless quail stuffed with black pudding my favourite. Nicola's front of house skills are exemplary and always a warm welcome. **Michelin Star. AA**🏵🏵 ●

Open: *All year ex 3wks Jan & 2wks Sept*	**Price Guide:**	*Lunch £20.00-£24.00 (2 or 3 Course)*
Closed Sun dinner, Mon all day, Tues lunch		*Dinner £35.00-£42.00 (3 or 4 course)*
Children: *Over 12*		*Sunday lunch £27.50*
Disabled: *Not suitable*	**Location:**	*Take road to Salcoats from A737 - 1 mile*
Covers: *24*		*and follow signs.*

THE THREE CHIMNEYS
AND THE HOUSE OVER-BY
Colbost, By Dunvegan, Isle of Skye. IV55 8ZT
Tel: 01470 511258   Fax: 01470 511358.
Email: eatandstay@threechimneys.co.uk   www.threechimneys.co.uk

Winner of numerous awards Shirley and Eddie Spears have forged an oasis of culinary excellence, in the middle of nowhere, which began with the renovation of the 100 year old cottage some 25 years ago. The consistency in the standard of cuisine over the years has been extraordinary. With the introduction of 6 suites in 1999 it took on a 'new look' – and developed into a 5 star VisitScotland 'Restaurant with Rooms'. De luxe suites with small verandah and panoramic views over Loch Dunvegan. Only a short distance from Dunvegan itself the area is abundant in natural food resources – fresh fish, game, lamb and venison – seafood a speciality. Perfect dining experience brilliantly executed by head chef Michael Smith. Eddie on hand with his vast knowledge of wines which adds to the experience. Situated 4 miles west of Dunvegan on the road to Glendale and under the watchful eye of the 'MacLeod Tables' you won't want to miss this one when on the Isle of Skye. Holder of the AA 3 rosette award for a number of years. **AA**

Open: *All year (ex. 2 weeks Jan)*	**Disabled:**	*Yes*	
No Rooms: *6 Suites*	**Covers:**	*30*	
TV in Rooms: *Yes*	**Price Guide:** *Double from £220.00 - £265.00*		
Room Tel. *Yes*	**Location:**	*B884, 4 miles West of Dunvegan on*	
Children: *Yes*		*Road to Glendale*	

ABSTRACT RESTAURANT
33-35 Castle Terrace, Edinburgh. EH1 2EL
Tel: 0131 229 1222
Email: reservations@abstractrestaurant.com   www.abstractrestaurant.com

This is the Edinburgh operation similar to the one in Inverness. No doubt at the cutting edge of fine dining, it's really good to experience the formal and professional restaurant scene. Apertif offered in the comfy bar, tasty canapes then to warm brown hare pie served with an apricot & apple chutney, red chard leaves and an Onuga caviar cream. Gamey flavour perfect. Main was sea bream with aubergine, tomato & a mussell & chive sauce. Pudding was a sort of biscuit cake with light rose flavoured ice cream. Great selection of freshly baked bread – the light brioche served with unsalted butter. Great coffee. All the staff appeared to be French but the promptness of service and explanations about the food were first rate. Very well positioned in Castle Terrace to accommodate the 'stockbroker' business etc.

Open: *All year*	**Disabled:**	*Yes*	
No Rooms: *N/A*	**Covers:**	*60*	
TV in Rooms: *N/A*	**Price Guide:**	*Lunch: from £12.95 Dinner: from £30.00*	
Room Tel. *N/A*	**Location:**	*Near the NCP car park in Castle Terrace.*	
Children: *Yes*		*Also near to Dundas & Wilson*	

DANIELS
88 Commercial Street, Leith, Edinburgh EH6 6LX
Tel: 0131-553 5933   Fax: 0131-553 3966
Email: danielsbistro@hotmail.com

I first met Daniel Vencker at the opening of L'Auberge in 1977. No doubt a pioneer of the gastronomic revolution in Scotland he offered the very best of French cooking at affordable prices. A native of Alsace he gained an enviable reputation which was recognised by all the major food guides. In 1996 he was on the move to his own Bistro style restaurant at Commercial Quay, Leith where the Scottish Office and waterfront development was taking place - perfect location. Although there is still the French influence in his cuisine he now offers a very expansive menu to cater for all tastes including traditional Scottish and Italian dishes complemented by fine wine from the various regions. Excellent value for money - a new concept and a new location. Don't miss this one when in Edinburgh.

Open: *All year*		**Disabled:**	*Yes*
No Rooms: *N/A*		**Covers:**	*60*
TV in Rooms: *N/A*		**Price Guide:**	*Lunch £7.75-£11.00*
Room Tel. *N/A*			*Dinner £16.00-£20.00*
Children: *Yes*		**Location:**	*Opposite Scottish Office HQ in Leith*

NUMBER ONE RESTAURANT
1, Princes Street, Edinburgh. EH2 2EQ
Tel : 0131 557 6727   Fax : 0131 557 3747
Email : numberone@thebalmoralhotel.com   www.roccofortehotels.com

Dinner at Number One this year was indeed a wonderful dining experience. One for 'the foodies' of that there is no doubt. Although part of The Balmoral Hotel the restaurant has created a reputation in its own right for fine dining - executive chef Jeff Bland whose culinary expertise is well known displays a quality of skills which have brought him recognition from many agencies and a number of awards. Jeff is equally at home with modern or traditional dishes - good combinations showing flair and imagination. High technical skills with some innovation, good texture and taste. There is a depth to the cusine here which is apparent throughout the meal. There can be no doubt that diners' expectations are fully realised - also a fine wine list available for the connoisseur. Ambience perfect with fine furnishings and white linen - sound advice and service impeccable. **Michelin Star**. Restaurant Manager: Gary Quinn. **AA**❀❀❀ 🍴

Open: *Closed first 2 weeks January*		**Disabled:**	*Access available*
Monday - Sunday: 6pm - 10.30pm		**Covers:**	*55*
No Rooms: *188*		**Price Guide:**	*3 course a la carte £55 (excluding wine)*
TV in Rooms: *Yes*	**Room Tel.** *Yes*		*Chef's Tasting Menu £60 (add £45 for wine pairings)*
Children: *Yes*		**Location:**	*1 Princes Street*

Craig Wilson - Head Chef
Eat On The Green

EAT ON THE GREEN

Udny Green, Ellon, Aberdeenshire. AB41 7RS
Tel: 01651 842337 Fax: 01651 843362
Email: enquiries@eatonthegreen.co.uk www.eatonthegreen.co.uk

An absolutely exquisite restaurant overlooking the village green at Udny Green not far from Ellon and close to Pitmedden gardens. In my view, the rural location adds to the anticipation of a night out with a good meal. I certainly wasn't disappointed – it had appeared 'on the radar' already with some excellent reviews. Layout of the dining area has been carefully planned to create an excellent ambience. Craig Wilson, chef/proprietor, is a highly skilled chef and at the time of writing Orry Shand his young sous chef had just won the prestigious 'Grampian Young Chef of the Year' award for a second year running. Lunch was a real enjoyable experience – all ingredients well sourced and cooked and front of house service faultless. Appears to attract interest from celebrities such as Lorraine Kelly (who refers to Craig in her autobiography as the kilted chef) and complimentary reviews are noted from the First Minister Alex Salmond and Sir Sean Connery. Repeat business is brisk which is the barometer of any good restaurant. Popular dinner menu on a Saturday night – always full. Phone is a must to reserve your table. Well recommended.

Open: *Closed Mon/Tues*		Covers:	*70*
No Rooms: *N/A*	TV in Rooms: *N/A*	Price Guide:	*Lunch: £19.00- £23.00*
Room Tel. *N/A*			*Dinner: a la carte Sat. only £45.00 (set price)*
Children: *Yes*		Location:	*A920 from Ellon. B999 from Aberdeen. (Near*
Disabled: *Yes*			*Pitmedden Gardens).*

STRAVAIGIN

28 Gibson Street, Hillhead, Glasgow. G12 8NX
Tel: 0141 334 2665 Fax: 0141 334 4099.
Email: bookings@stravaigin.com www.stravaigin.com

Now a household name in Glasgow Stravaigin has taken on a 'new look' – the traditional Scottish roots are still apparent with the introduction of a more classical and contempory style. Difficult to describe the ambience here – certainly different and unusual. Bistro bordering on fine dining with some really wonderful combinations. Chilean stew of seafood and meats with Scottish mussels, lamb and rabbit. Aberdeen Angus sirloin topped with cajun styled prawns could be your choice. Catering for an ever evolving customer who require something different it has become more evident over the years that tastes and trends are changing. Stravaigin has introduced this innovative style of fusion which attracts its faithful followers. Good 'front of house' with staff who have been here for a few years and an extensive wine cellar add to the dining experience. Other outlets include Stravaigin 2 in Ruthven Lane & The Liquid Ship on the Great Western Road. Good value for money.

Open: *All year ex. Xmas, New Year & Sundays*		Covers:	*76*
No Rooms: *N/A*		Price Guide:	*Dinner: from £34.00 3 courses*
TV in Rooms: *N/A*	Room Tel. *N/A*		*Lunch: from £12.95*
Children: *Yes*		Location:	*M8, junct 17 or A82 from city centre - Gt Western*
Disabled: *Unsuitable*			*road, turn down park road, rt into Gibson St., 200 yds on right*

FULLY INTEGRATED SOLUTIONS

Brodies offer a fully integrated coffee solution with a range of coffees roasted in our factory in Musselburgh matched to a comprehensive range of coffee machines from filter, to traditional & bean to cup machines.

We also blend a range of speciality teas and infusions and premium quality catering teas.

Our range includes a selection of In-room hospitality products as well as a comprehensive range of Fairtrade products.

Newhailes Industrial Estate, Newhailes Road, Musselburgh, EH21 6SY, Scotland, U.K.
Tel. No 0131 653 4010   Fax No. 0131 653 4020
email: sales@brodies1867.co.uk   www.brodies1867.co.uk

CRAGGAN MILL RESTAURANT & GALLERY

By Grantown-On-Spey, Morayshire. PH26 3NT
Tel : 01479 872288   Fax : 01479 872288
Email : info@cragganmill.co.uk   www.cragganmill.co.uk

Award winning chefs Graham Harvey & Sheila McConachie are really making a name for themselves in the Spey Valley. Idyllic situation just outside Grantown-on-Spey (on the Aviemore side) in an attractive rural setting. This old 18th century meal mill was lovingly restored in 1979 to facilitate all the comforts and ambience of a top dining experience. (Lunches too!) Cuisine could be described as traditional Scottish fayre but also classical French influence especially with their signature dish of Mussels, of which there are a number of combinations. A firm favourite. Extensive menus with mouth watering choice. Home made bread and ice cream. Graham & Sheila display a dedicated approach, using high quality ingredients. Well defined flavours and some innovative dishes. Front of house service perfect. Also making a name for themselves with the publication and success of the book 'The Whisky Kitchen' which contains 100 recipes. Don't go past this one when visiting the area.

Open: *All year except Tuesdays*		**Covers:**	*50*
No Rooms: *N/A*		**Price Guide:**	*Lunch £9.95 (2 courses)*
TV in Rooms: *N/A* **Room Tel.** *N/A*			*Dinner £18.00-£30.00 (3 courses)*
Children: *Yes*		**Location:**	*Outskirts of Grantown en route to Aviemore.*
Disabled: *Category 3 (VisitScotland)*			*Right hand side leaving Grantown - half mile.*

ABSTRACT RESTAURANT

20 Ness Bank, Inverness. IV2 4SF
Tel: 01463 223777 Fax: 01463 712378
Email: reception@glenmoristontownhouse.com   www.abstractrestaurant.com

An integral part of The Glenmoriston Town House this restaurant ranks as one of the finest in Scotland. This should be on your itinery, whether a 'foodie' or not – an experience not to be missed. Technical skills are obvious with ambition to create high standards and be consistent throughout all phases of the meal. I visit here regularly – combinations are quite exciting and different. No 'restricted' menu here – excellent choice of meat and fish dishes or the 7 course tasting menu. Red mullet, quail salad, lobster, spring Scottish lamb and Barbary duck just part of this choice. Flavour exemplary and expectations are fully met. The chef's table in the kitchen is innovation itself – great ambience with knowledgeable and attentive staff. A terrific wine list to boot. Ample car parking. *AA* 🏵🏵🏵

Open: *All year*		**Disabled:**	*Yes*
No Rooms: *30*		**Covers:**	*35*
TV in Rooms: *Yes*		**Price Guide:**	*Dinner from £34.00*
Room Tel. *Yes*			*Tasting Menu from £50.00*
Children: *Yes*		**Location:**	*Ness Bank 5 minutes from City Centre*

CHEZ ROUX RESTAURANT

Rocpool Reserve, Culduthel Road, Inverness. IV2 4AG
Tel: 01463 240089 Fax: 01463 248431
email: info@rocpool.com www.rocpool.com

To quote Albert Roux, " I want to create the kind of restaurant I remember from my home town, offering good and honest country cooking. The kind of place you can go to eat without ringing the bank for permission. Chez Roux will offer Scottish ingredients with a 'French Twist.' This is exactly what I experienced during my visit – head chef Davey Aspin (who has worked in many Michelin star establishments) allied with the talents of Albert Roux create some imaginative dishes, perfectly executed with faultless presentation. Exciting flavours (pike quenelle with lobster sauce a firm favourite) dominate – fish of the day & meat of day are standard options from the a la carte with sensible combinations. However, menus offer an excellent choice. Wonderful puddings. All, I should add, at a very modest price. Front of house operation efficient and informative if you're not sure - dishes are explained in French/English. Elegant and extremely comfortable dining room with views over the city. I would recommend The Chez Roux experience to everyone. Go for it.

Open: *All year*	**Disabled:** *Yes*
No Rooms: *11*	**Covers:** *32*
TV in Rooms: *Yes*	**Price Guide:** *Lunch: £10.00 - £25.00*
Room Tel. *Yes*	*Dinner: £15.00 - £30.00*
Children: *Over 8*	**Location:** *Culduthel Road, just up from Inverness Castle.*

THE GROUSE AND CLARET RESTAURANT

Heatheryford, Kinross. KY13 ONQ
Tel: 01577 864212 Fax: 01577 864920
Email: grouseandclaret@lineone.net www.grouseandclaret.com

The Grouse and Claret is really a country centre which combines accommodation, an art gallery and a fishery. It is very conveniently situated just off the M90 between Edinburgh and Perth in a rural setting - in fact there are 25 acres encompassing restaurant, art gallery, fishery and meadow. Over the last number of years chef/proprietor David Futong and his wife Vicki have earned an enviable reputation for quality cuisine in an ideal setting. The conservatory adds a new dimension - spacious dining area with views over the meadow. Menus are sensible and cater for all tastes - great emphasis on delicious home made food, beautifully presented - seasonal game and fresh shell fish including lobster and crayfish a house speciality. This is a wonderful setting for small weddings and functions. Comfortable detached bedrooms - some overlooking the trout ponds make this the ideal base in the country only a short drive from the city hazards of Edinburgh. Ample car parking.

Open: *All year ex. 1 wk. Jan; 10 days Oct.*	**Disabled:** *Yes*	**Covers:** *60*
Sun. night/all day Mon.	**Price Guide:** *B&B price per room: Double: £80.00;*	
No Rooms: *3 En Suite 3*	*Single: £50.00. Lunch £10.50-£20.00*	
TV in Rooms: *Yes* **Room Tel.** *No*	*Dinner £20.00-£35.00 (à la carte)*	
Children: *Yes*	**Location:** *Leave M90 Junction (6) then 500 yds -*	
	Private Road Opposite Service Station	

LIVINGSTON'S RESTAURANT

52 High Street, Linlithgow, West Lothian. EH49 7AE
Tel: 01506 846565 Fax: 01506 846565
Email: contact@livingstons-restaurant.co.uk www.livingstons-restaurant.co.uk

This is what you call a real hidden gem of a restaurant. A 'cottage' themed restaurant set in attractive gardens it is located through a vennel off the main street. Very impressed with the new extension which fits in so well with the original rustic type dining room. A family business in the true sense of the word, this is a great success story which has been built up by the Livingston family over a number of years. No compromise here - consistently high strandards of cuisine coupled with excellent front of house service. The culinary skills of head chef Chris McCall and his brigade are evident – excellent choice and combinations with vibrant flavours. Menu always changing to reflect the good use of seasonal fresh produce. Wine cellar of note. A thriving restaurant with a high percentage of repeat business. Once you have visited you will return - of that there is no doubt. Even just to taste Christine Livingston's tablet! Your hosts: Ronald, Christine and Derek Livingston. *AA* 🏵🏵

Open: *Closed Sun/Mon & 1st 2 weeks Jan and 1 week June & Oct*		**Children:** *Over 8 (evening)*	
No Rooms: *N/A*		**Disabled:** *Yes*	
TV in Rooms: *N/A*		**Covers:** *50*	
Room Tel. *N/A*		**Price Guide:** *Lunch £16.95-£19.95 Dinner £29.95-£36.95*	
		Location: *Eastern end of High Street opp. Post Office.*	

CREEL RESTAURANT WITH ROOMS

Front Road, St. Margaret's Hope, Orkney. KW17 2SL
Tel: 01856 831311
Email: alan@thecreel.freeserve.co.uk www.thecreel.co.uk

Although not quite on your doorstep this is a mecca for all who enjoy food prepared to consistently high standards on the south part of Orkney just over the Churchill Barriers and 14 miles from Kirkwall. Spent 2 nights with Alan and Joyce Craigie taking the Gillsbay Ferry directly into St. Margaret's Hope and a short drive to the 'restaurant with rooms'. Alternatively there is a ferry from Scrabster. There is complete dedication here - food prepared using much of the island produce but with originality, flair and imagination that reflect a high quality of culinary skills. It could be described as modern cooking with a hint of Orcadian influence. The Creel has 2 AA red rosettes and is rated highly in the Good Food Guide (UK). A bit of an adventure getting there but an experience not to be missed. *AA*🏵🏵 🐂

Open: *Closed Jan/Feb. and Mon. Open Apr-Sept & weekends Nov/Dec*	**Disabled:** *Unsuitable*	
No Rooms: *3 En Suite*	**Covers:** *34*	
TV in Rooms: *Yes* **Room Tel.** *No*	**Price Guide:** *B/B single from £65.00 B/B double from £95.00 Dinner: from £34.00*	
Children: *Over 5*	**Location:** *A961 South across Churchill barriers. 20 mins from Kirkwall*	

Craig Millar - Head Chef
The Seafood Restaurant, St. Andrews
(3 AA Rosettes)

DEANS @ LET'S EAT
77-79 Kinnoull Street, Perth. PH1 5EZ
Tel: 01738 643377   Fax: 01738 621464
Email: deans@letseatperth.co.uk   www.letseatperth.co.uk

You just can't beat this for consistency – as reported last year it just gets better and its good to see Chef Willie Deans on 'the floor' of the restaurant at lunch time having a wee blether with his patrons. Delightful cuisine with well sourced ingredients and executed to perfection. Dedication here which clearly shows an ambition to achieve high standards and consistent throughout all courses. Home made breads and ice cream. Careful attention with prep work produces a work of art, whether it's the lunch roast (different on 4 days of the week) or your choice from the a la carte you will not be disappointed. Excellent wine cellar. Flavours so well defined this is what I call a real dining experience. Spacious restaurant with plenty of 'elbow space' – clothed tables and arrangement just right. Terrific ambience prevails with the experienced front of house staff under the supervision of Margo Deans. Highly recommended. (Also see recipe at rear of The Good Food section). **AA** 🏵 🏵 🍽

Open: *All year except Sun/Mon*		**Disabled:** *Yes*	
No Rooms: *N/A* **En suite:** *N/A*		**Covers:** *60*	
TV in Rooms: *N/A*		**Price Guide:** *Lunch from £14.00 - £21.00*	
Room Tel. *N/A*			*Dinner from £22.00 - £35.00*
Children: *Welcome*		**Location:** *Corner Kinnoull/Atholl Street near North Inch.*	

THE SEAFOOD RESTAURANT
The Scores, St. Andrews, Fife. KY16 9AS   Tel: 01334 479475   Fax: 01334 479476
also at 16, West End, St. Monan's, Fife. KY10 2BX   Tel: 01333 730327   Fax: 01333 730508
Email: info@theseafoodrestaurant.com   www.theseafoodrestaurant.com

Having sourced both restaurants this is a dining experience you will not forget – you are already making plans to revisit as you leave. The premises at St. Andrews, all glass encased, is a wonder of modern architecture not far from the famous 18th green behind the club house. Both premises have stunning views to the sea – the interior design is fantastic (no expense spared). If you are into seafood, experience the culinary skills of co-owner/head-chef Craig Millar known to me for many years. Kilbrandon oysters, pan-seared collops of monkfish & lemon thyme panacotta - my favourite choice over the years. Cooked to perfection. Fresh ingredients to compliment each dish – some innovation here with vibrant flavours. Great wine cellar, perfect ambience and a total commitment by staff under the personal supervison of co-owner Tim Butler. A must for the connoisseur. **AA restaurant of the year - Scotland and Northern Ireland (2004-2005).** 3 AA red rosette award. **AA** 🏵 🏵 🏵

Open: *All year*		**Covers:** *60*	
No Rooms: *N/A*		**Price Guide:** *Lunch £20.00-£26.00*	
TV in Rooms: *N/A* **Room Tel.** *N/A*			*Dinner £35.00-£45.00*
Children: *Yes*		**Location:** *Pitching distance from R&A Clubhouse,*	
Disabled: *Yes*			*below the Scores*

Scottish quality salmon

Quality Approved
SCOTTISH SALMON

Naturally they're the best

www.scottishsalmon.co.uk

CREAGAN HOUSE WITH ACCOMMODATION

Strathyre, Perthshire. FK18 8ND
Tel: 01877 384638 Fax: 01877 384319
Email: eatandstay@creaganhouse.co.uk www.creaganhouse.co.uk

In the heart of Rob Roy country Creagan House was originally a farmhouse dating from the 17th. century but now restored and upgraded to provide a 'baronial' dining hall and 5 charming bedrooms - one a four poster. Strathyre, which means 'sheltered valley', is a village north of Callander and south of Balquhidder. Proprietors Gordon & Cherry Gunn create a real homely atmosphere. Known the Gunn family since 1990 and I can assure you of a warm welcome, excellent cuisine and very comfortable accommodation. Gordon is meticulous with his preparation and presentation. Using much of the local attributes of a rich arable Perthshire the menus include Gaelic fillet steak, fillet of venison, poached turbot with wonderful sauces and an excellent selection of seasonal vegetables. Home made desserts or Scottish cheeses are favourites. AA 2 red rosettes for food and a member of The Scotch Beef Club. **AA**❀❀ ★ 🐄

Open: *All year ex. Wed. & Thurs.*	**Disabled:**	*Yes*	
No Rooms: *5 En Suite*	**Covers:**	*15 Parties 35*	
TV in Rooms: *Yes*	**Price Guide:** *DB&B from £89.00*		
Room Tel. *No*		*B&B from £60.00*	
Children: *Yes*	**Location:**	*Just north of Strathyre village between*	
		Callander & Lochearnhead	

DEANES

36-40 Howard Street, Belfast. BT1 6PF
Tel: 02890 331134
Email: info@michaeldeane.co.uk www.michaeldeane.co.uk

Although the main fine dining experience remains in Howard Street, Michael Deane has expanded his 'empire' considerably over the years. Now with further outlets to cater for all (including bistro) he will launch his new seafood restaurant by the time this book is published. A great success story from the time I met him in Scotland in 1988. His exhuberant style - both of showmanship and of uncompromisingly perfectionist cooking has elicited praise from the sternest of food critics and the most demanding food guides. Reluctant to classify his food - there are perceptible French, Pacific Rim, British and Irish influences in a typical menu - Michael Deane believes that it is the chef's imperative to set trends, rather than follow them. The secret is never to cease to innovate. From his beginnings at Claridges Michael has been on a pilgrimage - always propelled by his pure passion for food and its possibilities. **Michelin Star** and AA 4 red rosettes. Keep this one in mind and follow this entry whenever in Belfast. **AA**❀❀❀❀

Open: *Closed Sun.-Tues.*	**Disabled:**	*Brasserie only*	
No Rooms: *N/A*	**Covers:**	*35*	
TV in Rooms: *N/A* **Room Tel.** *N/A*	**Price Guide:** *Dinner: £65.00 (2 courses) - £80.00*		
Children: *Welcome*		*Lunch: Brasserie - from £20.00*	

Pan fried Brisbane Mains Lamb Loin with Herb Polenta, Pea Puree and Madiera Jus

Ingredients:

Polenta Cake:

340g Polenta
500ml Chicken Stock
700ml Water
175g Butter
45g Parmesan
Salt and Pepper to taste
Garlic
6 cloves
4 stalks of Rosemary

Pea Puree:

1kil of peas
500ml of chicken stock
250g butter
Half a packet of marjoram

Fresh Peas:

Blanched Fresh Peas
Shallots Sliced
Fresh Mint
Salt and Pepper

Madiers Jus:

Black Peppercorns
Shallots
Carrots
Celeriac
Leeks
(all finely chopped)
Madiera 300ml
Red Wine 300ml
Veal Jus 400ml

Method:

Polenta:

Bring stock, garlic and herbs to boil. Sieve into a bain-marie, then rain in the polenta. Whisk for 10 t5 mins until polenta is cooked. Take off the heat, beat in parmesan, butter fresh herbs and season to taste. Spread on a tray to about 1 inch thickness. Leave this to rest and cut when cold. Pan fry to order until crispy golden colour.

Pea Puree:

Bring herbs and stock to the boil, then add in the peas. Cook for 2 to 3 mins. Pass stock out of the peas using a sieve. Liquidise peas and season and add stock to correct thickness (should be to a soft peak).

Jus:

Chop vegetables finely, crush peppercorns – sweat off these gently in butter until veg is golden brown. Add Madeira, Red Wine, and reduce by 2/3. Add veal stock and reduce by half. Pass through muslin.

Head Chef: Darin Campbell
Fortingall Hotel, Fortingall, Aberfeldy, Perthshire
(also see entry page 33)

Fillet of Halibut on a Cauliflower and Truckle Cheddar Puree, Paprika Poached Potatoes, Leeks and Courgette Tempuras with Fennel Veloute

Ingredients:

Fillet of Halibut:
4 x 150g fillet halibut
Oil for cooking
Salt and black pepper

Paprika Poached Potatoes:
8 rate potatoes, shaped
Light fish stock infused
with lemon gras

Courgette Tempura:
Nibbed almonds
1 courgette

Batter:
1 small bottle sparkling water
Dash vinegar
Self raising flour to thicken
Salt and pepper

Cauliflower Puree:
1 medium cauliflower
50 g truckle cheddar
1 dspt sp grain mustard
1 small onion finely chopped
1 clove garlic, crushed
Nob of butter
125 ml chicken stock

Leeks:
White & green of leek,
(retain top for stock)
Lemon zest, Butter, Fish stock

Fennel:
1 large bulb of fennel,
peeled & trimmed
(retain trimmings for stock)
Fish stock to cover
Pinch of saffron

Method:

Cauliflower Puree:

Remove outer leaves from cauliflower, slice and place into a pan adding the chicken stock, cover with a tight fitting lid and cook until tender. Chop up the cauliflower. Melt the butter adding the onion, garlic and Cauliflower, cover with a lid and sweat for 5 minutes without colour, add the cauliflower stock, replace lid and cook on a low gas until tender and dry. Add the mustard and cheese, allow to melt then blitz until smooth, check seasoning and keep warm.

Potatoes:

Cover the potatoes with stock adding paprika and lemon gras trimmings, cook until tender, finish with butter

Leeks:

Cut the leeks in 2 dividing into white and green, cut both into large dice, wash well. Cook white with lemon zest in a little stock, half way through cooking add the green of the leek and finish with butter, salt and pepper.

Batter and Courgette:

Place the water into a clean bowl adding the vinegar, lightly thicken with the flour. Cut the courgettes thinly into triangles, pass through flour into butter with nuts, deep fry at 190°C until crisp, season.

Sauce and Fennel:

Slice the peeled fennel thinly, place trimmings in a pan and cook down by half with the stock, pour over the sliced fennel and cook until tender with the saffron. Finally add the cream and thicken with the butter.

To Finish:

Season and pan seal the halibut and cook, spread the cauliflower puree onto the plates, add the leeks and rest the fish on top, add the braised fennel, juices and courgette fritters, finally add the potatoes and serve.

Proprietor/Chef: Willie Deans
Deans @ Let's Eat, 77-79 Kinnoull Street, Perth
(also see entry page 81)

Summer Isles Langoustines with Garlic Butter on a Herb Risotto

(Serves 4)

Ingredients:

12 large, live langoustines
90g (3oz) Arborio rice
1/2 small onion, finely chopped
1/2 stick celery, finely chopped
1/2 glass dry white wine
1 sprig fresh rosemary, finely chopped
500ml (1pint) chicken stock
1 tbsp flat leaf parsley, chopped
1 tbsp grated parmesan cheese
1 small clove garlic, crushed
30g (1oz) butter
olive oil
sea salt

Method:

In a large saucepan, boil a couple of litres of salted water. Add 2 bay leaves, 1/2 a sliced lemon and a pinch of black peppercorns. Drop the langoustines into the water, bring back to the boil and cook for a further minute. Drain the langoustines and leave to cool. When cool, remove the langoustines from their shells, remembering to peel off the gritty intestinal tract! Put to one side, but do not refrigerate!

Heat the stock in a saucepan.

In a heavy-based saucepan, fry the chopped onion, celery and rosemary in a little olive oil for about 5 minutes, or until soft.

Now add the rice and wine and a couple of ladlefuls of the hot stock. Stir constantly until the liquid has been absorbed. Add more stock and repeat the process. Keep adding the stock until the rice is 'al dente': this may take 20 minutes or so. About 15 minutes into cooking the rice, gently heat the garlic

butter in a frying pan and toss in the prawns - warm them for about half a minute. When the rice is cooked, remove from the heat and stir in the chopped parsley and the grated parmesan.

To Serve:

Spoon the risotto onto 4 plates and carefully lay 3 prawns on the top of each.

Head Chef: Chris Firth Bernard
Summer Isles Hotel, Achiltibuie, Ross-shire
(also see entry page 19)

Fresh Fruit Flan with Raspberry Coulis

Pate Sucre – sweet paste:
200g soft/plain flour
125g unsalted butter
50g caster sugar
1 egg

Method:
Place butter, sugar & flour into bowl and rub in until the mixture looks like breadcrumbs. Add the egg and mix to a smooth dough. Pin out the paste in 10 equal pieces, line 10cm individual flan tins and bake at 180C for approximately 8mins until lightly browned.

Crème Patissiere - pastry cream:
250ml milk
250ml double cream
100g castor sugar
6 egg yolks
25g soft/plain flour
20g custard powder
2 vanilla pods

Method:
bring milk, cream and vanilla to the boil. Whisk the sugar and yolks, mix in the flour and custard powder. Add the liquid, return to a clean pan and re-boil for about 10 seconds.

Fresh Raspberry Coulis:
1 large punnet fresh raspberries
juice of 1 lemon
50g castor sugar

Method:
liquidise all ingredients and pass through a chinoise, chill.

Pineapple Glaze:
250ml pineapple juice
juice of ½ lemon
juice of ½ orange
1 star anise
250g castor sugar
10g arrowroot

Method:

Dilute arrowroot in a little cold water. Boil all other ingredients. Thicken the mix with the arrowroot. Pass and chill.

Assembly:

Allow pastry cases to cool, fill level with creme patisserie. Arrange cut fruits of your choice neatly on top brush with pineapple glaze. Present with fresh coulis.

Pastry Chef: Paul Clelland
Uplawmoor Hotel & Restaurant, Neilston Road, Uplawmoor, Renfrewshire
(also see entry page 34)

Pan Seared Seabass with
Goats Cheese Gnocchi and Apple Puree

1 sea bass fillet cut into 4/5 pieces depending on the size. Use 3 pieces per portion for a starter.

Apple Puree:
1kg granny smiths peeled and cored
100g sugar
50g butter
20g apple sours
green food colouring

Peel and core apples then cut into even pieces. Put the sugar in an already warm pan. When sugar is a caramel, add apples, butter and sours and cook until apples are very soft. Blitz and add food colour until required colour pass.

Goats Cheese Gnocchi:
1kg potato
350g pasta flour
4 egg yolks
100g goats cheese
parmesan
salt and pepper to taste

Cook potatoes on a bed of rock salt for 2/3 hours until completely cooked. Push through sieve then dry in oven 4/5 mins. Add yolks and cheeses and knead until smooth. Over season slightly. Add the flour and check seasoning and roll into shape. Add to boiling water then turn down heat. Cook slowly then refresh in ice water. Dry cover in olive oil, lay on j cloths and use when required.

Goats Cheese Froth:
200g milk
70g goats cheese
2g lecithin
salt

Put goats cheese and milk into a pan and heat up 60°. Take off heat, cling film and leave to infuse. Add lecithin then blitz. Do not heat up above 80° when serving. Froth with hand blender.

Lemon Oil:

250ml lemon scented oil
250ml groundnut oil
200ml white wine vinegar
1 clove of garlic
2tsp salt
1tsp pepper

Mix all together and put in jars. Use as needed

Garnish:
Apple salad (julienne of red apple. Dress with lemon oil)
Dressed pea shoots
Lemon oil
Goats cheese froth

Head Chef: Craig Gibbs
Cringletie House, Peebles, Peebleshire
(also see entry page 54)

STEVENSONS

SCOTLAND'S
GOOD HOTEL AND FOOD BOOK
2010

Order Form: **Alan Stevenson Publications**
Fala, 20 West Cairn Crescent, Penicuik,
Midlothian EH26 0AR
Tel: 01968 678015
Fax: 01968 679898
E-mail: alan@stevensons-scotland.com

Date: .... Please mail .... Copies of

Stevensons, Scotland's Good Hotel and Food Book, 2010.

Your Name: ....

Address: ....

.... Postcode: ....

Retail Price	1 Book	2-5 Books	6 + Books
United Kingdom	£8.00	£7.00 each	p.o.a.
USA only	$18.00	$14.00 each	p.o.a.
Canada only	$20.00	$15.00 each	p.o.a.
Europe	£8.00	£7.00 each	p.o.a.
Euro Zone	€14.00	€12.00 each	p.o.a.
Outside Europe	£12.00	£10.00 each	p.o.a.

Post & Packaging	1 Book	2-5 Books	6 + Books
United Kingdom	£2.00	£5.00	p.o.a.
USA/Canada	$9.00	$11.00	p.o.a.
Europe	£4.00	£7.50	p.o.a.
Euro Zone	€6.50	€10.00	p.o.a.
Outside Europe	£5.00	£4.00	p.o.a.

All orders outwith United Kingdom consigned by airmail. Payment in pounds sterling, please, payable to Alan Stevenson Publications - alternatively online at www.stevensons-scotland.com

No. of Copies: ...... at £/$/€ .... each. Total £/$/€ ....

Post & Packaging Total £/$/€ ....

I enclose a Cheque/Bank Draft Total **£/$**/€ ....

Hotels continued

Restaurants listed alphabetically by name

INDEX

Hotels listed alphabetically by name

See contents page 4 for list of Trade Sponsors.